HA-HA

THE
TERRIFIC TRIPLE TITLE
SERIES

ACTING, ACTING, ACTING
ALASKA, ALASKA, ALASKA
AMERICA, AMERICA, AMERICA
DANCERS, DANCERS, DANCERS
DANGER, DANGER, DANGER
DISASTER, DISASTER, DISASTER
DOCTORS, DOCTORS, DOCTORS
DOGS, DOGS, DOGS
FUN, FUN, FUN
GHOSTS, GHOSTS, GHOSTS
HORSES, HORSES, HORSES
INDIANS, INDIANS, INDIANS
JOKES, JOKES, JOKES
LOVE, LOVE, LOVE
MORE JOKES, JOKES, JOKES
MORE SPORT, SPORT, SPORT
NURSES, NURSES, NURSES
PATRIOTISM, PATRIOTISM, PATRIOTISM
PIRATES, PIRATES, PIRATES
PRO, PRO, PRO
PUNS, PUNS, PUNS
RIDDLES, RIDDLES, RIDDLES
SCIENCE, SCIENCE, SCIENCE
SPACE, SPACE, SPACE
SPEED, SPEED, SPEED
SPORT, SPORT, SPORT
WESTWARD, WESTWARD, WESTWARD
WITCHES, WITCHES, WITCHES
YOUTH, YOUTH, YOUTH

Jokes, Jokes, Jokes

Selected by HELEN HOKE

Illustrated by

RICHARD ERDOES

FRANKLIN WATTS, INC.
575 Lexington Ave., New York 22, N. Y.

Copyright 1954 by Franklin Watts, Inc.
Fourteenth Printing
Manufactured in the United States of America
by the Montauk Book Mfg. Co., New York
Library of Congress Catalog Card Number: 54–9827

Contents

About This Book–

Putting together a book of jokes is no laughing matter! It gets to be hard *work*. The more jokes I gathered, the less I laughed. Sometimes I smiled a bit, but mostly I was pretty glum. I think I was glum because no matter how funny *I* thought a joke was, I always met with up with people who couldn't see it for dust. Nevertheless, I persevered, and somehow, since this book was finished, I have found myself laughing quite a lot—even at the jokes in JOKES, JOKES, JOKES.

While I was compiling the book I often thought to myself, "This is a joke on *you!*" And now I want to tell you how I went about playing this joke on myself: first, I wrote down all the jokes I knew, and separated them into categories. Next, I began collecting jokes from everyone I knew. Finally I got together thousands of jokes on 3 x 5″ cards. Meanwhile I had written and asked practically everyone I knew out of town to send me jokes.

They did, and I almost went out of my mind. I had to write polite "thank-you" notes to each of these good friends, even when they sent me stories I already had, or that weren't suitable for this particular book.

But some people *did* take pains to try to understand what sort of book I had in mind. These people I thank from the bottom of my heart, for their jokes were the best. And

also I want to thank the many young people who came into my path during the long spring and summer while I was working on this book. My, those kids were patient. They winnowed the mass of cards into the best selection possible, I believe. I asked these luckless boys and girls to put *one* paper clip on the cards containing jokes they liked, and to put *two* paper clips on the ones they thought particularly awful. When the cards came back to me, I threw out all those with two paper clips on them. (I saved the clips.)

I threw out those cards even when they held jokes which *I* thought were wonderfully funny—and maybe that's when I felt the glummest. But since JOKES, JOKES, JOKES was to be for *readers* and not for *me*, that's what I had to do and I did it.

In the process I discovered all sorts of things about what I had long fancied my own pretty fair sense of humor. I can see now why people like Fred Allen, the Marx Brothers, Burns and Allen, and sometimes even Sid Caesar and Danny Kaye look occasionally harassed.

RICHARD ERDOES' hilarious drawings were a real help to me in thinking again that jokes were jokes. Those pictures *are* funny, and I haven't found one person to disagree about that!

Helen Hoke

FOR MY SON JOHN,

who made my life miserable,
some years ago, with the jokes
from just such a book as this.

Jokes,
     Jokes,
          Jokes.

Absent-Minded
Antics

ABSENT-MINDED PROFESSOR: "Lady, what are you doing in my bed?"
LADY: "Well, I like this bed, I like this neighborhood, I like this house, and I like this room. And anyway, I'm your wife!"

A farmer who was on his way home from market had the feeling that he had forgotten something; but what it was he couldn't figure out.

As he neared home this conviction increased to such a degree that he stopped his horses two or three times, scratched his head in perplexity, and tried to recall what he had forgotten, but in vain.

At last he reached home and was met by his daughter, who looked at him in surprise and cried, "Why Father, what have you done with Mother?"

•

Did you hear about the absent-minded professor who:

Returned from lunch and saw a sign on his door, "Back in 30 minutes," and sat down to wait for himself?

Slammed his wife and kissed the door?

Got up and struck a match to see if he had blown out the candle?

•

The absent-minded professor had been married only a short time. One evening upon arriving home at his usual time, he found his wife acting cool toward him.

"What is the matter, dear?" he asked worriedly.

"Well George, you didn't kiss me when you left this morning," she said.

"Oh, darling," he said in wonderment. "Then who *was* it that I kissed?"

Did you hear about the absent-minded professor who held an egg in his hand and boiled his watch?

●

"Where is the car?" demanded Mrs. Stevenson, as her husband came up the front steps.

"Dear me!" exclaimed Professor Stevenson. "Did I take the car out?"

"You certainly did. You drove it to town."

"How odd! I remember now that after I got out I turned around to thank the gentleman who gave me the lift and wondered where he had gone."

●

Two absent-minded professors were driving home in an automobile.

"Say," one said, "be sure to turn out for that bridge that's coming down the road toward us."

"What do you mean, *me* turn out?" the other said, surprised. "I thought *you* were driving."

●

The absent-minded professor staggered from a train, his complexion very white.

"Riding backwards for ten hours," he explained. "I never could stand that."

"Why," his wife inquired, "didn't you ask the person sitting opposite to change seats with you?"

"I couldn't do that," said the professor. "There wasn't anybody there."

Did you hear about the absent-minded professor who fell overboard and forgot he could swim?

•

The phone rang about 2 A.M. and the absent-minded professor answered it. "Hello," he said.

THE VOICE: "Is this Dexter eleven eleven?"

PROFESSOR: "No, this is Dexter one one one one."

THE VOICE: "Oh—I am sorry to have bothered you!"

PROFESSOR: "It's quite all right. I had to get up to answer the phone anyhow."

G. I.
Jibes

The farmer watched the paratroop maneuvers with evident interest. Finally, one of the paratroopers landed in a tree near by. The farmer watched the soldier as he cut himself away from his harness and scrambled down.

"Boy," said the G.I., "that was something."

"Sure was," drawled the farmer. "First time I ever did see a man climb down a tree without climbing up first."

7

SUPPLY OFFICER: "Does the new uniform fit you?"
RECRUIT: "The jacket isn't bad, sir, but the trousers are a little loose around the armpits."

•

SOLDIER SAM: "Don't bother me. I am writing to my girl."
SOLDIER DAN: "But why are you writing so slowly?"
SOLDIER SAM: "She can't read very fast."

•

GUARD: "Halt! You can't go in there."
PRIVATE: "Why not?"
GUARD: "Because it's the General's tent."
PRIVATE: "Then what's it doing with that big sign 'PRIVATE' on the door?"

•

ADMITTING OFFICER (examining recruit): "Have you any scars on you?"
RECRUIT: "No, sir, but I can give you a cigarette."

•

The soldier was a mess. His trousers were covered with mud and stains. As he was walking along the company street with a pail, an officer stopped him.

"Just where do you think *you're* going, soldier?"

"To get some water," was the reply.

"In those trousers?"

"Don't be silly, sergeant," replied the G.I. "In the pail."

☺ 8

Young Tom told his father that when he grew up, he wanted to drive a big army tank.

"Well, Son," said his dad, "if that's what you want to do, I certainly won't stand in your way."

•

"Without a doubt, you're the stupidest guy in the service," roared the officer.

"Can't help it," replied the recruit. "I was born that way."

"All right, just answer me two simple questions," continued the officer. "First—what would happen if one of your ears were shot off?"

"That's easy, sir," replied the G.I. "I wouldn't be able to hear."

"Okay," said the irritated officer. "Next—then what would happen if *both* your ears were shot off?"

"Then I couldn't *see*," answered the recruit promptly.

"What do you mean, you couldn't *see*?" the officer yelled.

"Well, sir," explained the G.I., "if my ears was both shot off, my helmet would slide down over my eyes."

•

GENERAL, on inspection tour: "Why do you keep scratching yourself?"
PRIVATE: "I'm the only one who knows where it itches, sir."

9

RECRUIT: "Shall I mark time with my feet, sir?"
SERGEANT, sarcastically: "My good man, did you ever hear of marking time with your hands?"
RECRUIT: "Yes, sir! Clocks do it."

•

BOASTFUL SOLDIER, at a party: "The bullet struck my head and went careening into space."
BORED FRIEND: "You're being honest about it, anyway."

•

HANK: "They tell me when I'm in the saddle I'm a part of the horse."
YANK: "Yes, but did they tell you what part?"

•

What did the drum say to the drummer boy?
If you beat me, I'll call out the troops.

School Daze

BIG BROTHER: "Well, Joe, how do you like school?"
JOE: "Closed!"

●

TEACHER: "You can be sure that if Moses were alive today, he'd be considered a remarkable man."
LENNY: "He sure ought to be, he'd be more than 2,500 years old."

A small boy went to a school picnic, but it hardly met his expectations. He was stung by a bee; he fell into a creek; a little girl pulled his hair; he got badly sunburned. As he arrived home, limping and with torn and muddy clothes, his mother greeted him and asked, "Well, Son, what kind of time did you have at the picnic?"

"Mom," Sonny replied slowly, "I'm so glad I'm back, I'm glad I went."

●

TEACHER: "Yes, Sammy, what is it?"

SAMMY: "I don't want to scare you, but Pop said if I didn't get better grades, someone is due for a licking."

●

"What's the difference between a freshman and a senior?"

"Well, a freshman knows what he wants, and a senior knows he can't have it."

●

VISITOR: "What's your boy going to be when he finishes his education?"

DISCOURAGED PARENT: "An octogenarian, I think."

●

TEACHER: "How many sexes are there?"

SAMMY: "Three."

TEACHER: "Three! Can you name them?"

SAMMY: "Male sex, female sex, and insex!"

The teacher was trying to impress upon her students the advantages of peace. "How many of you young people object to war?" she asked. Up went several hands.

"Sammy, will you tell the class why you object to war?"

"Because wars make history," replied Sammy promptly.

●

TEACHER, to tardy student: "Why are you late?"

BARRY: "Well, a sign down the street said—"

TEACHER, interrupting: "Now what can a *sign* possibly have to do with it?"

BARRY: "The sign said: 'School ahead; go slow.'"

●

TEACHER: "Paul, can you tell me the name of an animal that travels great distances?"

PAUL: "Yes. A goldfish. It travels around the globe."

13

TEACHER: "Name five things that contain milk."

BARRY: "Butter, cheese, ice cream, and—and—two cows."

●

TEACHER, brightly: "As we walk out-of-doors on a cold winter's morning and look about us, what do we see on every hand?"

SECOND-GRADERS, in unison: "Gloves!"

●

GEORGIE: "Teacher, would you scold anybody for something they didn't do?"

TEACHER: "Of course not. But why, Georgie?"

GEORGIE: "Well, I didn't do my arithmetic!"

●

TEACHER: "That's a comet."

LITTLE EDDIE: "A what?"

TEACHER: "A comet. *You* know what a comet is?"

LITTLE EDDIE: "No."

TEACHER: "Don't you know what they call a star with a tail?"

LITTLE EDDIE: "Sure—Mickey Mouse."

●

TEACHER: "What are the people of New York noted for?"

CHARLIE: "For their stupidity."

TEACHER: "Where ever did you get *that* idea?"

CHARLIE: "It says here in this book that the population of New York is very dense."

Little Betty was crying bitterly. Teacher asked what was the matter.

BETTY: "Oooh! My new shoes *hurt* me!"

"Well, no wonder," explained Teacher, "you have them on the wrong feet."

But Betty kept right on crying. "I *haven't* any other feet!" she cried.

●

TEACHER: "Jasper, I can scarcely read your handwriting. You *must* learn to write more clearly."

KID: "Aw, what's the use? If I wrote any better, you'd start complaining about my spelling!"

●

TEACHER: "Name three collective nouns."

HORACE: "Fly-paper, waste-basket, and vacuum-cleaner."

One rainy day poor Miss Kindergarten Teacher spent over a half hour pulling galoshes onto wet little feet, getting the children ready to go home. When she came to little Johnny, his galoshes took several minutes to struggle him into. Finally they were on.

"Thank you, Teacher," said Johnny. "You know, Teacher, these galoshes aren't mine."
Poor teacher groaned, sat Johnny down again, and pulled and pulled until his galoshes came off again. "Now then," she asked patiently, "whom *do* these belong to?"

"My brother," explained Johnny. "But my mother makes me wear them anyhow."

●

"Are your mother and father in?" asked the visiting teacher of young Billy, who opened the door.

"They *was* in," he explained, "but they is out just now."

"They *was* in. They *is* out. Shame on you! Where's your grammar?"

"She's gone to the store," explained Billy, "for some cat meat."

●

TEACHER (answering the phone): "You say George Gage has a bad cold and can't come to school? Who is this speaking?"
VOICE (with assumed hoarseness): "This is my father."

ARITHMETIC TEACHER: "If I gave you two apples and told you to give one to your brother, would you give him the little one or the big one?"

GEORGIE: "Do you mean my *little* brother, or my *big* brother?"

•

FRESHMAN: "But I don't think I deserve a zero on this paper."

PROFESSOR: "Neither do I, but it's the lowest mark I can give you."

•

SAMMY: "Do you think anyone can predict the future with cards?"

DANNY: "My mother can. She takes one look at my report cards, then tells me exactly what will happen when my dad gets home."

•

BIGGER BOY: "What are you doing with a pencil and paper?"

LITTLE BOY: "I'm writing a letter to my brother."

BIGGER BOY: "Who're you kidding? You know you don't know how to write."

LITTLE BOY: "Sure, but my brother doesn't know how to read, either."

•

TEACHER (teaching the alphabet): "What comes after *O*?"

DOPEY: "Yeah!"

17

How many books can you put into an empty school bag?

> *One, because after that is in, the bag won't be empty.*

•

TEACHER: "Tell me the truth now, who really did your homework?"
JOHNNIE: "My father."
TEACHER: "All alone?"
JOHNNIE: "No, I helped him with it!"

•

BOASTFUL COLLEGE COUSIN: "I'm taking three courses in college: French, Spanish, and algebra."
HIGH SCHOOL COUSIN: "Okay—let me hear you say good evening in algebra."

•

TEACHER: "What do hippopotamuses have that no other animals have?"
JACKIE: "Little hippopotamuses."

18

GEORGIE: "What part of the body is the fray?"

TEACHER: "What part of the body is the fray? What are you talking about?"

GEORGIE: "Well, right here in the history book it says—the general was shot in the thick of the fray."

●

"I guess I've lost another pupil," said the professor as his glass eye rolled down the kitchen sink.

●

TEACHER: "This composition on 'Our Cat' is, word for word, the same as your brother's."

TOMMY: "Yes, ma'am, it's the same cat."

●

GEORGE: "I want to buy a pencil."

CLERK: "Hard or soft?"

GEORGE: "Hard. It's for a stiff exam."

●

The teacher had been reading to her class about the rhinoceros family. "Now name some things," she said, "that are very dangerous to get near to, and that have horns."

"Automobiles," promptly answered Lenny.

TEACHER: "If we breathe oxygen in the daytime, what do we breathe at night?"
GRACIE: "Why, nitrogen, of course!"

•

TEACHER: "Explain the manners and customs of the natives of Borneo."
PUPIL: "They ain't got no manners and they don't wear no customs."

•

Exam question: "What's the best way to prevent infection caused by biting insects?"
DOPEY's answer: "Don't bite any."

•

A tutor who tooted a flute
Tried to teach two young tooters to toot.
    Said the two to the tutor,
    "Is it harder to toot, or
To tutor two tooters to toot?"

TEACHER: "Why are you late, George?"

GEORGE: "Sorry, Teacher. It was late when I started from home."

TEACHER: "Then why didn't you start early?"

GEORGE: "But Teacher—by that time it was too late to start early."

●

PAUL, about the new boy in the class: "His name is George, but we call him Flannel."

SAUL: "His name is George, but you call him Flannel? I suppose you call him Flannel for short?"

PAUL: "No, because he shrinks from washing."

●

TEACHER: "Kitty, what would you do if a man-eating tiger were chasing you?"

KITTY: "Nothing—'cause I'm a girl!"

●

TEACHER: "If you have ten potatoes and must divide them equally among seven persons, how would you do it?"

SAMMY: "I'd mash them."

●

Little Peter came home from school and said to his mother,

"Our teacher is really dumb. For four days she has asked us how much is two and two. We told her it was four. But she still doesn't know it; this morning she asked again."

A teacher called for sentences using the word "beans."

"My father grows beans," said the bright boy of the class.

"My mother cooks beans," said another pupil.

Then a third popped up: "We are all human beans."

●

TEACHER: "At your age I could name all the Presidents—and in the proper order."

BOBBY: "Yes, but there were only three or four of them then."

Pun Points

WOMAN (opening door of a refrigerator and finding a rabbit inside): "What are you doing there?"
RABBIT: "This is a Westinghouse, isn't it?"
WOMAN: "Yes."
RABBIT: "Well, I'm just westing."

LAWYER: "When they tried him the judge let him go free."
FRIEND: "Why?"
LAWYER: "The robber was deaf."
FRIEND: "What has that got to do with it?"
LAWYER: "Well, don't you know that you can't convict a man without a hearing?"

•

ANDY: "Al is the first person you learn about when you go to school."
SANDY: "Al who?"
ANDY: "Alphabet."

•

Mama Gnu was waiting for Papa Gnu as he came home for dinner one evening. "Our little boy was very bad today," she declared. "I want you to punish him."

"Oh, no," said Papa Gnu. "I won't punish him. You'll have to learn to paddle your own gnu."

•

"There's a hair in my coke," complained the teenager.

"That's quite possible," retorted the soda jerk. "I just finished shaving the ice."

•

If you put three ducks into a crate, what would you have?

A box of quackers.

The Eskimo was telling a story while sitting on a cake of ice. He finished. "Well, my tale is told," he lisped, as he stood up with his back to the fire.

●

HUGHIE: "Gee, I'd like to meet that swell-looking girl over there. Who is she, anyway?"
LOUIE: "Oh, she belongs to the Nodding Club."
HUGHIE: "What's that?"
LOUIE: "Nodding doing."

●

BABY EAR OF CORN: "Mamma, where did I come from?"
MAMMA EAR OF CORN: "Hush, darling, the stalk brought you."

●

TEACHER: "Give me a sentence with the word 'vermin' in it."
DOPEY: "Before I go fishin' I go vermin'."

●

LITTLE ROBBIE: "Doctor, I've just been bit by a dog."
DOCTOR: "Well, was he a rabid dog?"
LITTLE ROBBIE: "No sir, doctor. He was just a plain old bird dog."

●

PAUL: "What kind of cake is that?"
MOM: "It's marble cake. Want a piece?"
PAUL: "No, I'll just take it for granite."

GARAGE MECHANIC: "The horn on your car must be broken."
MOTORIST: "No, it's just indifferent."
MECHANIC: "What do you mean, indifferent."
MOTORIST: "It just doesn't give a hoot."

●

Sign on a Japanese bakery wagon in Yokohama:

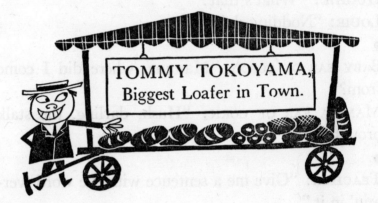

TOMMY TOKOYAMA,
Biggest Loafer in Town.

DOLLY: "What are you doing with your socks on inside out?"
MOLLY: "My feet got too hot, so I turned the hose on them."

●

You tell 'em, Butcher . . . you've got lots of tongue!

●

HABERDASHER'S CLERK: "These are especially strong shirts, madam. They simply laugh at the laundry."
CUSTOMER: "No, thank you! I know that kind; I had some which came back with their sides split."

DOPE: "Do you know who owned the smallest radio in the world?"

DUNCE: "No, who owned the smallest radio in the world?"

DOPE: "Paul Revere—he broadcast from one plug."

●

MEDIEVAL MAMMA: "Hast Sir Knight ast ye for thy hand in wedlock?"

DAUGHTER: "Not yet, Mamma, but the knight is young."

●

FIRST CANNIBAL: "Am I late for chow?"

SECOND CANNIBAL: "Yes, everybody's eaten."

●

Why shouldn't a doctor be seasick?

Because he is accustomed to see sickness.

●

Why does an Indian wear feathers?

To keep his wigwam.

●

RONNIE: "I see in the paper that a guy ate six dozen pancakes."

JOHNNIE: "Oh, how waffle!"

●

HORACE: "What would a cannibal be who ate his mother's sister?"

MORRIS: "I'll bite—what?"

HORACE: "An aunt-eater, of course."

TEACHER: "Thomas, construct a sentence using the word 'archaic'."
TOMMY: "We can't have archaic and eat it, too."

•

"I guess your brother was pleased when he found himself the father of twin boys," said one neighbor to another when they met on the bus.

"Was he! He went around grinning from heir to heir."

Pal
Patter

LEADER OF THE GANG: "I'll give you to understand my father is a big man. He's a Lion, a Moose, and an Elk."

ONE OF THE GANG: "Gee—how much does it cost to see him?"

●

BUSTER: "That your dog?"

RUSTY: "Yes, he used to be a pointer but my mother spoiled him."

BUSTER: "How?"

RUSTY: "She taught him it wasn't polite to point."

29

PAUL: "That cake you're eating looks good."

SAUL: "It *is* good."

PAUL: "It makes my mouth water."

SAUL: "To show you what a good guy I am, here's a blotter."

•

LITTLE HARRY: "I don't like what you said and I'll give you five minutes to take it back!"

BIG BARRY: "Yeah, and what if I *don't* take it back in five minutes?"

LITTLE HARRY: "Well, then I'll give you longer."

•

COLLEGE FRESHMAN: "Had a tough time raising this mustache."

COLLEGE SOPHOMORE: "Well, crops are bad everywhere this year."

•

HUGHIE: "Hey! Why are you wearing my raincoat?"

LOUIE: "You wouldn't want your best suit to get wet, would you?"

RANDY: "Did you fill in that blank yet?"

ANDY: "What blank?"

RANDY: "The one between your ears."

•

RANDY: "What would you do if you were in my shoes?"

SANDY: "Polish them!"

30

Farmer
Fare

They walked down the lane together,
the sky was covered with stars;
They reached the gate in silence,
he lifted down the bars.
She raised her brown eyes to him,
there's nothing between them now;
For he was just a farmer's boy,
and she—a Jersey cow!

31

FARMER, to deaf hired man: "Abner, where's that mule I told you to take out and have shod?"
NEW HAND: "Did you say 'shod'? *I* thought you said *'shot'*. I've just been buryin' her."

•

A farmer was walking down Main Street when he saw a sign over a plumbing supply store. It said, CAST IRON SINKS.

"By Jiminy!" he said. "Anyone knows that!"

•

A farmer's wife shipped a crate of eggs to a wholesale house in a city, but before doing so she wrote on one of the eggs: "I got 5 cents for this egg. What did you pay for it?"—to which she signed her name and address.
Months later she received a letter from an actor, on very fancy stationery.

"My dear Madam," he wrote, "while playing the lead in a Shakespearean play recently, I received your egg for nothing."

•

Young Philip had just come back from an agricultural college. He was showing off to the neighboring farmer. "Your farming methods are so old-fashioned," he said. "Why, I bet you don't get ten pounds of apples from that tree."

"I daresay you're right," said Farmer Putney. "That there's a pear tree."

Mom and Pop Potter went to the big city. In an antique shop they saw a Swiss cuckoo clock. They stood and watched it for a half hour, while the shop owner turned it back and forth to make it cuckoo. Finally Pop Potter asked the price.

"Fifty-two dollars."

"We'll think it over," Pop told the owner, and thanked him for his kindness.

Several months later, Pop Potter had gathered together enough money to buy the cuckoo clock, and he sent to the city for it, as a surprise present for Mom Potter's birthday.

A big package came—right on the very day of Mom Potter's birthday—and they had the time of their lives with it. Every hour and half-hour, on the minute, they rushed in from their work around the farm, to see and listen to the cuckoo speak.

That night in bed, Pop Potter listened, along with Mom, till two o'clock, then was so sleepy he couldn't stay awake any longer.

At three A.M., suddenly the cuckoo clock made a sort of whirring sound, the cuckoo rushed out and cuckoo'd once, twice, seven times—then, finally, eighteen times!

"Wake up! Wake up!" shouted Mom Potter, as she shook Pop Potter violently. "Wake up and *do* something, Pa! It's later than I ever knowed it to be before!"

33

A stingy farmer was reproving his hired man for carrying a lantern to go calling on his best girl.

"Why, when I was courtin' I didn't need to carry a lantern," he said.

"Yeah—and look what *you* got," the hired man retorted.

●

The embarrassed city hostess said to her country cousin: "I thought I suggested you come after supper."

"Right," said the country cousin, "that *is* what I came after."

●

FARMER BOY: "My Pop can't decide whether to get a new cow or a tractor for his farm."

CITY BOY: "He'd certainly look silly riding around on a cow."

FARMER BOY: "Yeah, but he would look a lot sillier milking a tractor!"

●

A farmer was trying hard to fill out a railway company claim sheet for a cow that had been killed on the track. He came down to the last item: "DISPOSITION OF THE CARCASS." After puzzling over the question for some time, he wrote: "Kind and gentle."

Catty Quips

JEAN: "Bob didn't blow his brains out when you rejected him, after all. He came right around and proposed to *me*."

JOAN: "Well, he must have gotten rid of them some other way, then."

LITTLE JOAN, at dancing school: "You'd be a fine dancer except for two things."
JOHN: "What?"
JOAN: "Your feet!"

•

POLLY, annoyed at a tale-bearing classmate: "People should call you 'Amazon'."
MOLLY: "Why?"
POLLY: "Because you're so wide at the mouth."

•

The reason a dog has so many friends is that his tail wags instead of his tongue.

•

NELL: "Do you think that Jack would be happy with a girl like me?"
BELLE: "Maybe—if she wasn't *too* much like you."

•

MRS. PRETTY: "Whenever I'm in the dumps, I get a new hat."
MRS. MEAN: "Oh, so *that's* where you get them!"

•

FIRST SORORITY SISTER: "Is Marguerite a good partner in bridge?"
SECOND SORORITY SISTER: "She was awful. You couldn't tell by the expression on her face how she would play."
FIRST SORORITY SISTER: "Poker face?"
SECOND SORORITY SISTER: "No, but I wanted to."

SALLY: "Well, I'm falling in love and I think I should go to a palmist or a mind reader. Which would you suggest?"

HALLIE: "You'd better go to a palmist—you *know* you've got a palm."

●

BABS, about the pretty new neighbor girl: "She must be very musical."

MABS: "How can you tell?"

BABS: "By the cords in her neck."

●

BILL: "Last night I met a girl and fell in love at first sight."

PHIL: "Why don't you invite her to the prom?"

BILL: "I took a second look."

●

PATTY: "Where did he meet her?"

HATTIE: "They met in a revolving door and he's been going around with her ever since."

●

BETTY: "I'm sorry—I quite forgot your party the other evening!"

BETSEY: "Oh, weren't you there?"

●

A boring classmate spoke to the class favorite, Peggy, one bright Monday morning.

"I passed your house yesterday," she said.

"Thanks. We appreciate it," retorted Peggy.

37

PAUL: "Last night I told my girl, 'I'm going to kiss you tonight or die in the attempt!' "
SAUL: "Well, did you?"
PAUL: "You didn't see my name in the obituary column this morning, did you?"

●

HARRY: "Please give me a kiss."
CARRIE: "My lips are chapped."
HARRY: "Well, one more chap won't hurt them."

●

POLLY: "Say, Molly, will you loan me a dime. I want to call a friend."
MOLLY: "Here's thirty cents, call *all* your friends."

●

EDYTH: "She said your hair was dyed."
REDYTH: "It's false!"
EDYTH: "That's what *I* told her."

●

MOLLY, showing a picture of her beau: "I hooked him on the pier last Saturday night."
POLLY: "Oh? Well, I think you should have thrown him right back."

Riddle
Rumpus

What two letters of the alphabet contain nothing?

> *M. T.*

What kind of coat is made without sleeves and put on wet?

> *A coat of paint.*

What is the difference between a cloud and a boy who is being spanked?

> *One pours rain; the other roars with pain.*

39

Why is a snake a careless animal?
He loses his skin.

●

If you lived in a cemetery, with what would you open the gate?
With a skeleton key.

●

What is it that is black and white and red all over?
A book.

●

When should any pig be able to write?
When he has been turned into a pen.

●

What part of a fish weighs the most?
The scales.

●

Which is the strongest day of the week?
Sunday, because all the rest are weak days.

●

When is a hat not a hat?
When it becomes a pretty girl.

●

Why does Uncle Sam wear red-white-and-blue suspenders?
To hold his pants up.

●

Why is the sea restless?
Because it has rocks in its bed.

What did the big hand on the watch say to the little hand?

I'll be around in an hour.

•

What kind of serpents are like babies' toys?

Rattlers.

•

When is a piece of string like a stick of wood?

When it has knots in it.

•

What is it that we have in December that we don't have in any other month?

The letter D.

•

On which side does a chicken have the most feathers?

The outside.

•

Why is a healthy boy like the United States?

Because he has a good constitution.

•

When you lose something why do you always find it in the last place you look?

Because you stop looking when you find it.

•

What is the difference between a prizefighter and a man with a cold?

One knows his blows, and the other blows his nose.

I occur once in every minute, twice in every moment, and yet not once in a billion years. What am I?

The letter M.

●

Why does a dog turn around several times before lying down?

Because one good turn deserves another.

●

When do 2 and 2 make more than 4?

When they make 22.

●

What keeps the moon in place?

Its beams.

●

Why should fish be better educated than bugs?

Because they live in schools.

●

When is a piece of wood like a king?

When it is made into a ruler.

●

What did the big chimney say to the little chimney?

"You're too young to smoke."

●

At what time of day was Adam created?

A little before Eve.

●

Why are pianos like good people?

Because they are upright, grand, and square.

For how long a period of time did Cain hate his brother?

>As long as he was Abel.

•

Why is your hand like a hardware store?

>It has nails.

•

When does a boat show affection?

>When it hugs the shore.

•

What city is a small stone?

>Little Rock.

•

Who dares to sit before the Queen of England with his hat on?

>Her chauffeur.

What is everybody doing at the same time?
Growing older.

•

What is it that is always behind time?
The back of a clock.

•

What is the difference between here and there?
The letter T.

•

If twelve make a dozen, how many make a million?
Very few.

•

Why is a dog's tail like the heart of a tree?
Because it's farthest from the bark.

•

When is the time of the clock like the whistle of a train?
When it is two to two.

•

What is horse sense?
Just stable thinking.

•

Why was the giant Goliath very much astonished when David hit him with a stone?
Because such a thing had never before entered his head.

Gloomy Gertie
and Gloomy Gus

GLOOMY GERTIE: "I've been asked to get married lots of times."

GLOOMY GUS: "Who asked you?"

GLOOMY GERTIE: "My mother and father."

●

GLOOMY GUS: "I've got a brother with three feet."

GLOOMY GERTIE: "What do you mean?"

GLOOMY GUS: "Well, my mother got a letter from my brother who's away at school and he said: 'You would hardly know me—I've grown three feet.'"

GLOOMY GERTIE: "What did you get that little silver medal for?"

GLOOMY GUS: "For singing."

GLOOMY GERTIE: "What did you get that big gold medal for?"

GLOOMY GUS: "For stopping."

●

GLOOMY GUS: "I like George; he's different from the other boys my sister knows."

GLOOMY GERTIE: "Different? How?"

GLOOMY GUS: "Well, he's willing to go out with her."

●

Gloomy Gertie is so modest she pulls down the shade to change her mind.

●

GLOOMY GERTIE: "I'm going home—I expect a phone call."

GLOOMY GUS: "From whom?"

GLOOMY GERTIE: "I don't know."

GLOOMY GUS: "Then how do you know the phone will ring?"

GLOOMY GERTIE: "Because I'm going to take a bath. The phone almost always rings while I'm in the tub."

GLOOMY GUS: "That's right! I've noticed myself how the phone generally rings while I'm taking a shower."

GLOOMY GERTIE: "Yeah, but sometimes I have to take two or three baths to make it ring."

46

"Gloomy Gertie just has no style," complained a classmate.

"How come?" asked another.

"Well! Did you see those baseball stockings she wore all last week?"

"*Baseball* stockings?"

"Yes! They had four runs in them."

●

Gloomy Gertie finally got tired of all her girl friends saying she was bound to be an old maid.

"Listen! I can marry anyone I please," she said.

"Why *don't* you, then?" said one of the girls.

"I don't please anybody."

●

"Why do you go steady with Eloise?" asked Gloomy Gus's father.

"She's different from other girls," said Gloomy Gus, "*quite* different."

"How so?"

"She's the only girl who will go with me."

●

Gloomy Gus calls his car "Baby," because it never goes without a rattle.

●

As soon as Gloomy Gus found out that little things count, he had to quit swiping from his kid brother's piggy bank.

47

GLOOMY GERTIE, suspiciously: "I think he plans to marry me for my money."

CANDID FRIEND: "Well, if he does, he'll have earned it."

•

Gloomy Gus failed in all his exams this spring.

"What's the meaning of this?" asked his teacher.

"It's not my fault," explained Gloomy Gus. "The guy who usually sits beside me was home sick that day."

•

"I get blamed for everything that goes on around here. Even as a baby, they were always pinning things on me," said Gloomy Gus.

Ah, Women!

MRS. GUSH, lighting the candles: "Have a look at this cake I decorated for my birthday party. Don't you think my sense of design is wonderful?"

MRS. MEOW: "Yes, but your arithmetic is terrible."

"What would be the first thing you'd do if you had hydrophobia?" asked one teacher of another.

"I'd ask for a pencil and some paper."

"To make your last will?"

"No," replied the other wearily. "To make a list of the people I want to bite."

•

A woman visiting the aquarium asked an attendant, "Can you tell me whether I could get a live shark here?"

"A live shark?" said he in surprise. "Whatever could you do with a live shark?"

"A neighbor's cat has been eating my goldfish, and I want to teach him a lesson."

•

JUNIOR DEVIL: "Heh, heh, heh."

SATAN: "What are you laughing at?"

JUNIOR DEVIL: "I just locked a woman in a room with a thousand hats and no mirror."

•

The toastmistress at a banquet introduced Thomas Alva Edison, mentioning his many inventions and dwelling at length on the talking machine. The aged inventor then rose to his feet, smiled, and said gently: "I thank the lady for her kind remarks, but I must insist upon a correction. God invented the talking machine. I only invented the first one that can be shut off."

Little Percival's mother moved to a small town where there was no private school. She reluctantly took her precious child to attend public school.

On the first day of school, she gave the teacher a long list of instructions. "My Percival is ever so sensitive," she explained. "Don't ever punish *him*. Just slap the boy *next* to him. That will frighten Percival quite enough!"

•

On what day of the year do women talk the least?
The shortest day.

•

GRATEFUL MOTHER: "Were you the one who saved my little boy from drowning?"
LIFEGUARD: "Yes."
MOTHER, angrily: "Well, where's his cap?"

•

"What could be more sad," mused the sentimental professor, "than a man without a country?"

"A country without a man," answered the pretty girl.

•

"Now, Johnny," coaxed his mother, "be a good boy and say 'Ah-h-h,' so the nasty doctor can get his finger out of your mouth."

A woman got on a bus. "Does this bus go to Parkview Boulevard?" she asked Pat, the driver.

"Yes," replied Pat.

A few minutes passed. "Are you *sure* it goes to Parkview Boulevard?" the lady asked again.

"Yes," replied Pat.

"There's no danger we'll go past Parkview Boulevard, is there?"

"No," said Pat.

Every two minutes she asked him about Parkview Boulevard.

"Will you *tell* me when we're near it?"

"Yes!"

"Just how will I *know* when we get to Parkview Boulevard?"

Pat finally exploded. "By the smile on me face, lady!"

Home, Sweet Home

A very high-pressure vacuum-cleaner salesman was forcing a home demonstration on a prospective customer. He took a large paper bag out of his case, and proceeded to scatter the contents all over Mrs. Whipple's beautiful living-room rug—coffee grounds, lint, gravel, dust, eggshells, and all sorts of dirt. Then he said, "Madam, I'll eat every bit of this stuff that my vacuum cleaner doesn't pick up."

Mrs. Whipple started out of the room.

"Where are you going?" asked the salesman.

"To get you a knife and fork," she said. "You see, we don't have electricity."

53

The music professor in a small town met Pop Parker on the street, carrying a long music case.

PROFESSOR: "Oh, Mr. Parker, I see you've bought a saxophone."

POP PARKER: "No, I just borrowed it from the man next door."

PROFESSOR: "But why did you want to do that? You can't play it, can you?"

POP PARKER: "No, but neither can the man next door, while I've got it."

●

MOM PARKER, to the new hired girl: "Hannah, have you given the goldfish fresh water today?"

HANNAH: "No, ma'am. They haven't finished the water I gave them yesterday."

●

"I must say these are fine biscuits!" exclaimed the young husband.

His wife's mother looked at him severely. "How can you say they are fine, when you know they are not?" she asked.

"I didn't say they were fine," said the young husband. "I merely said I must say so."

●

MOM PARKER, to the new maid: "Be careful not to drop those china dishes, Maggie."

MAGGIE: "Don't you worry, ma'am. If they did fall they're too light to hurt my feet!"

Two of the little Parker boys had a favor to ask of their mother.

"You ask her," said Paul, ten.

"No, it would be better if you did," answered Peter, six. "You've known her longer than I have."

●

A young bachelor was entertaining a young lady for dinner at his apartment. As his Chinese servant served coffee she asked him: "Ling Lee, how do you make such delicious coffee?"

"Him take plentee boil water and stir in coffee velly, velly slow," explained the servant.

"Yes, but it's always so clear! How do you strain it so cleverly?" questioned the guest.

"Him take master's silk socks . . ." the servant started to say.

"What!" gasped his master. "You take my best silk socks to strain the coffee?"

"Oh, no, master," replied the servant, "him never take master's *clean* socks."

●

"Freddie," said his mother. "I wish you would run down the street and see how old Mrs. Cheever is this morning."

"Okay," Freddie agreed, and soon he returned and reported.

"Mrs. Cheever says it's none of your business how old she is."

55

On a card in the front window of a suburban house appeared the following notice: "A piano for sale." In the window next door, another card appeared bearing just one word: "HURRAH!"

●

FIRST NEIGHBOR: "What's the idea of the Smiths taking French lessons?"

SECOND NEIGHBOR: "They have adopted a French baby, and want to understand what she says when she begins to talk."

●

A peddler knocked at the door of a housewife.

"I sell all kinds of things for the house. Do you want to buy something?"

"No, I don't want anything," said the housewife firmly.

"Maybe a pan or a pot?"

"No, I don't want anything. Now, get going. I don't want anything."

"Maybe a clothes brush?"

"No, I don't want anything!"

"Maybe a vacuum cleaner?"

"I don't want *anything*. Get going!"

"Maybe a tablecloth? Some hairpins? I've got all kinds of things."

"Now, listen to me. If you don't get going, I'll whistle for a policeman."

"Do you want to buy a whistle?"

😊 56

"People who say they sleep like a baby," says Pop Parker, "usually never had one."

●

When are houses like books?
When they have stories in them.

●

Why are trees in winter like troublesome visitors?
Because it's a long time before they leave.

●

Mrs. Richmoney's new maid, Norah, had a very bad habit of interrupting her mistress with unimportant household problems, usually just when Mrs. Richmoney was right in the middle of a telephone chat, or serving tea to the Friday Afternoon Club ladies. One day just after Norah had interrupted a particularly important party, Mrs. Richmoney warned her that if she ever did it again, she could pack her things and leave immediately.

The very next day, Mrs. Richmoney was in the midst of a bridge game, and Norah appeared in the doorway, gesturing and about to speak. Mrs. Richmoney waved her back, finished the game, excused herself, and stepped into the kitchen to talk to Norah.

"I'm glad to see you understand that I meant what I said yesterday. Now tell me, what's on your mind?"

"Well, ma'am," said Norah, "I just wanted to tell you that the house is on fire."

57

RALPH: "I'm homesick."
LOUIS: "But don't you live at home?"
RALPH: "Yes, but I'm sick of it."

●

A man met a friend he hadn't seen for a long time.
  "Why, George," he said, "you've changed!
  What's making you look so old?"
  "Trying to keep young," said George.
  "Trying to keep young?" queried the man.
  "Yes," was the gloomy response, "nine of
  them."

●

POP PARKER, to a friend at work: "Well, we've managed to furnish three of the rooms in our house with the soap coupons my wife collects."
FRIEND: "Furnished three rooms by collecting soap coupons? Aren't you going to furnish the other three rooms?"
POP PARKER: "No—they're full of soap."

●

Summer is the dreaded season when youngsters, for no earthly reason, will slam, until they almost splinter, the doors they didn't close all winter.

 58

Squelch Squibs

The fresh young fellow in the barber shop kept asking the pretty manicurist for a date. She repeatedly said "No."

Finally, the young man insisted: "Well, *why* won't you go out with me?"

"Because I'm engaged," replied the pretty manicurist.

"What difference does that make?" quipped the eager young smart-aleck. "Ask your fiancé."

"Ask him yourself," the manicurist retorted. "He's shaving you."

The quiet Martin family lived in a city apartment building right next to the noisy Bangs family, who gave very lively parties several nights a week. The Martins suffered the racket quietly for some time, until one day Mr. Martin noticed the air duct which ran through from the Bangs's living room to the Martins' living room. This gave Martin a fine idea about how to get even.

The next night a noisy party was going on next door. Martin quietly removed the grille over his air duct, and, reaching in, scotch-taped the microphone of his home recording machine to the Bangs's air duct. He let it record a good hour's hilarity.

The next night, when he knew the Bangses would be going to bed very early, to make up for staying up so late the night before, he put the loud-speaker of his machine where the microphone had been the night before, turned up the volume, and really let the Bangses have it.

The Martins haven't had any trouble since.

●

The butcher was busy waiting on a customer when a woman rushed in, pushed through the waiting customers to the counter, and demanded: "Give me a pound of cat food, quick!"

Turning to the other customers she said, "I hope you don't mind my getting waited on before you."

"Not if you're *that* hungry," a woman retorted.

BERNIE: "We've got a hen down at our house that lays white eggs."
ERNIE: "What's so wonderful about that?"
BERNIE: "Can *you* do it?"

●

Leonora's new beau was far from modest in relating his exploit.

"I shot this tiger in India," he said, "under terrific odds; it was a case of me or the tiger."

"Well, the tiger certainly makes the better rug," agreed Leonora boredly.

●

The loquacious old gentleman boarded a transport plane and started a conversation with the pilot.

"This plane takes all my courage," he said, "I was almost killed twice in an airplane."

"Once would have been enough," replied the bored pilot.

●

LATE-STAYING GUEST: "Well, good night. I hope I have not kept you up too late."
YAWNING HOST: "Not at all. We would have been getting up soon, anyway."

●

PHOTOGRAPHER, to an extremely disagreeable and fussy customer: "Look pleasant, please. As soon as I snap the picture, you can resume your natural expression."

"This table," said Mrs. Richmoney, "goes back to Louis the Fourteenth."

"You don't have a thing on me," replied her maid. "My dining-room set goes back to Sears Roebuck on the thirteenth."

●

JOHNNY, at breakfast: "Dad, today is Lincoln's birthday. My, he was a great man, wasn't he?"
POP, always eager to teach his young son a lesson: "Yes, Son, indeed he was. And mind you," he added pompously, "when Abraham Lincoln was *your* age, he was out splitting rails."

"Yes, Dad, I know," retorted Johnny. "And when he was *your* age, he was President of the United States."

●

FUSSY LADY in the fish market, haughtily: "I don't like the looks of that codfish."
FISHMONGER, sarcastically: "Well, if it's looks you're after, why don't you buy a goldfish?"

Baby Talk

MOTHER: "Did you thank Mrs. Porter for the lovely party she gave?"

LITTLE DOROTHY: "No, Mommie, I didn't. The girl leaving just before me thanked her and Mrs. Porter said, 'Don't mention it,' so I didn't."

One day Johnny's father brought his boss home with him for dinner.

After being served, young Johnny paused, and for a moment studied his plate intently, then asked his mother if the meat on his plate was mutton.

"No, that is roast beef, Johnny," she replied. "Why do you ask?"

"Because Daddy said he was going to bring a muttonhead home for dinner with him this evening."

63

ANDY: "How's your uncle doing with his farm?"

SANDY: "Not so good. There ain't so much money in milk and eggs any more. So he sits up all night trying to think of something else for the hens and cows to do."

•

TEACHER: "I hear you've got a new baby over at your house, Robert."

ROBERT: "Well," hesitatingly, "I guess he *is* new— but from the way he cries, you'd think he had had a lot of experience!"

•

BARBER: "Well, son, how would you like your hair cut?"

SMALL BOY: "Just like Dad's, and be sure to leave that little round hole on the top where his head comes through."

•

ED: "What goes 999 thump! 999 thump! 999 thump?"

NED: "I dunno. What?"

ED: "A centipede with a wooden leg."

•

LITTLE GIRL: "My big brother has a new invention, and it's very practical, too."

NEIGHBOR: "What is it?"

LITTLE GIRL: "He makes the chickens swim in hot water so they'll lay hard-boiled eggs."

☺ 64

ALEX: "We've got an animal family."
FELIX: "How's that?"
ALEX: "Well, Mother's a dear, Sister's a lamb, I'm a kid, and Dad's the goat."

●

Why does a horse eat the least of all the animals?
> *Because he eats best when there isn't a bit in his mouth.*

●

BILL: "Is it bad luck to have a cat follow you?"
PHIL: "It depends. Are you a man or a mouse?"

TOMMY: "Say, Mom, was our baby sent down from heaven?"
MOTHER: "Yes, son."
TOMMY: "I guess they like to have things quiet up there, huh?"

DOCTOR'S SON: "*My* pop makes his money easy. All he does is look at a person, talk to him, then write something down—and he gets five dollars."

LAWYER'S SON: "*That's* nothing, *my* pop sits in his office. Someone comes in. He tells them he'll look it up in a book, and then he gets fifty dollars."

MINISTER'S SON: "Oh, but after *my* dad gets up to talk it takes six men to bring the money down the aisles!"

•

MOTHER: "Now Eddie, you must not be selfish. You must let your little brother have the sled half the time."

EDDIE: "But Mother, I do. *I* have it going down the hill, and *he* has it coming up."

•

The little city girl was on her first visit to the country. She was quite impressed by the cows, pigs, and chickens. But when she saw the peacock, she was amazed.

"Look," she gasped, "a rooster in full bloom!"

•

Mother was telling stories of the time she was a little girl. Little Reggie listened thoughtfully as she told of having a Shetland pony and a cart, going to a country fair, and wading in the brook on the farm.

Finally he said with a sigh, "Gee! I wish I had met you earlier, Mom."

Daddy was showing Junior the family album and came across the picture of himself and his wife on their wedding day.

"Was that the day Mom came to work for us?" Junior inquired.

•

Little Georgie was given two dimes one Saturday evening. "One of the dimes," said his father, "is for Sunday school tomorrow, and the other is for an ice-cream cone for yourself."

As Georgie ran to the drug store to get his ice-cream cone, he stumbled and one of the dimes rolled into the sewer drain. "Oh dear," said Georgie, "there goes the Lord's dime!"

•

"How is your Aunt Tilly?" a neighbor woman asked little Paul.

"She had her appendix taken out the other day," Paul informed her.

"Did they give her anything for it?"

"No," answered the literal-minded child, "it wasn't worth anything."

•

GRANDMA: "And were you a good little girl at church this morning, Susie?"

SUSIE: "Oh, yes, grammaw! A nice man offered me a big plate full of money, but I said, 'No, thank you, sir.'"

67

A kind neighbor stopped little Dopey on his way to school and said, "That's an interesting pair of socks you have on—one blue and one yellow."

"Yes," answered Dopey eagerly. "And the funny thing is, I've got another pair just like it at home!"

•

Two little girls were playing on the front porch when one of them ran into her house, was gone a moment, then came back out carrying two big red apples.

"Just look what Grannie gave us!" she cried. The other girl looked puzzled. "Grannie? What's a Grannie?" she asked.

"A Grannie," said the first little girl, "is an old lady who keeps your mother from spanking you."

•

A sturdy little boy ran by a policeman on the block at top speed. Five minutes later he rushed by again as fast as the first time. After this had happened a half-dozen times, the policeman stopped him and asked, "What's the idea, Sonny? What's the rush?" The boy looked up very indignantly and shouted, "I am running away from home!"

"Oh," said the policeman. "But you've gone around this same block at least five times."

"I know it!" shouted the boy over his shoulder as he started running again. "My mom won't let me cross the street."

NEIGHBOR: "Where have you been, Betty?"

BETTY: "To Sunday school."

NEIGHBOR: "What's that paper in your hand?"

BETTY: "Oh, just an ad about heaven."

●

VISITOR: "What was your Mommy's name before she was married?"

LITTLE PAUL: "I think it must have been 'Statler'— that's the name on most of our towels."

●

BIG SISTER: "Bobby, if you eat the rest of that pumpkin pie, you'll burst!"

BOBBY: "Okay. Pass the pie and get outa the way."

●

JONATHON: "Mother, was that policeman over there ever a little baby?"

MOTHER: "Why, certainly. Of course."

JONATHON: "Oh, I would just *love* to see a baby policeman!"

●

Young Tommy greeted his sister's boy friend enthusiastically:

> "That mouth organ you gave me for my birthday is absolutely by far the best present I've ever had."
>
> "I'm glad you like it."
>
> "Yes—Mother gives me a quarter a week not to play it."

69

JAKE: "I et six eggs for breakfast this morning."
TEACHER: "You mean ate, don't you?"
JAKE: "Well, maybe it *was* eight I et."

●

FRIEND OF THE FAMILY: "Well, Charles, how do you like your new little sister?"
CHARLES: "Oh, she's all right, I guess; but there are lots of things we needed worse."

Animal Crackers

The keeper of the zoo found the new employee standing uneasily before the lion's cage.

KEEPER: "Didn't I tell you that when a lion wags his tail he's friendly?"

EMPLOYEE: "Yes, but he was roaring and wagging his tail at the same time."

KEEPER: "Well, what's that got to do with it?"

EMPLOYEE: "I didn't know which end to believe."

What is it that has four legs, eats oats, has a tail, and sees equally well from both ends?

A blind mule.

●

What are the two flowers that should decorate the zoo?

A dandelion and a tiger lily.

●

OLD HEN: "Let me give you a piece of good advice."

YOUNG HEN: "What is it?"

OLD HEN: "An egg a day keeps the ax away."

●

Two leopards were having lunch and one sat back and sighed contentedly, "Mmmm, just hit the right spots!"

●

PAPA KANGAROO: "Anabelle, where's the baby?"

MAMA KANGAROO: "My goodness! I've had my pocket picked!"

What animal took the most luggage into the Ark, and what animal took the least?

> *The elephant took his trunk; and the rooster had only a comb.*

●

Why is a watchdog bigger by night than he is by day?

> *Because he is let out at night and taken in in the morning.*

●

The teacher took her class to the zoo. When they passed the lion's cage, she asked, "What's the plural of lion?"
One of the boys answered, "Lions."

"What's the plural of sheep?" she asked.
One of the girls answered, "Sheep."

"Right," said the teacher.
A little farther along they came upon a hippopotamus.

"What's the plural of hippopotamus?" the teacher asked little Johnny.
Johnny shuddered. "*Who* would want two of *those*?"

●

FIRST NEIGHBOR: "What were all your chickens doing out in front of your house early this morning?"
SECOND NEIGHBOR: "They heard some men were going to lay a sidewalk and they wanted to see how it was done."

ADMIRING HORSEWOMAN: "How did your horse happen to win the race?"
JOCKEY: "Well, I just kept whispering in his ear:
'Roses are red, violets are blue—
horses that lose are made into glue!' "

●

A teacher was giving her class a test in natural history.

"Now Johnny," she said, "tell me where the elephant is found."
Johnny thought a minute.

"The elephant," he said at last, "is such a big animal it hardly ever gets lost."

●

TEACHER: "Millie, spell the word 'mouse'."
MILLIE: "M-o-u-s."
TEACHER: "But what's at the end of it?"
MILLIE: "A tail."

●

"Now boys," said the teacher, "tell me the signs of the zodiac. You first, Thomas."
"Taurus, the Bull."
"Right! Now you, Harold, another one."
"Cancer, the Crab."
"Right again. And now it's your turn, Albert."
The boy looked puzzled, hesitated a moment, and then blurted out, "Mickey, the Mouse."

Dopey Dames

Mr. Simpkins: "You sure made a poor job of painting this door."

Mrs. Simpkins: "Well, you declared only this morning that it needed painting badly."

FEMININE VOICE on phone: "Hello, City Bridge Department?"

MASCULINE VOICE: "Yes. What can we do for you?"

FEMININE VOICE: "How many points do you get for a little slam?"

•

COUNTRY HOSTESS to visitor: "Are you interested in art?"

CITY VISITOR: "Yes, whenever I visit a strange city, the first thing I do is look up an artery."

•

"I hear your grandson has a new automobile," said the neighbor. "What make is it?"

"I'm not sure," replied Grandma, "but I think he said it was a LALLAPALOOZA."

•

GRANDMA: "And how did Georgie do on his history examination?"

MOTHER: "Oh, not at all well. But it wasn't his fault. Why, they asked him about things that happened before he was born!"

•

"Are you the game warden?" asked a lady over the telephone.

"Yes, I am the game warden," was the reply.

"Oh, I am so glad," said the lady. "Will you please suggest some games for a little party I'm giving for my children?"

76

DORA: "Why didn't you ride in the Bridle Path?"
NORA: "I thought that was only for newly married couples."

•

MRS. BUTLER: "Did you meet your son at the station?"
MRS. WILKINS: "Oh, goodness no! I've known him for years."

•

NEIGHBOR: "I understand your son is on the football team. What does he play?"
MOTHER: "I think he's one of the drawbacks."

•

THEATER USHER: "How far down do you want to sit, madam?"
"Why, *all* the way, of course."

•

"Now, this plant," explained the horticulturist patiently to the vague sightseer, "belongs to the begonia family."
"Ah, yes," chirped the sweet old lady, "and you're looking after it for them while they're away on vacation?"

•

MISTRESS: "Selma, when you wait on the table tonight for my guests, please don't spill anything."
HIRED GIRL: "Don't you worry, ma'am, I never talk much."

77

FISH DEALER: "Lobsters, madam; nice lobsters? Look, they're all alive."

LADY SHOPPER: "Yes, but are they *fresh*?"

●

A tobacco farmer was showing a visiting lady around his plantation.

> "These are tobacco plants in full bloom," he explained.
>
> "Isn't that wonderful!" she gushed. "And when will the cigars be ripe?"

●

A not overly bright woman swept into a fashionable kennel shop. "I want a collar for Wilbur," she said. Timidly, the clerk inquired, "What size, please?"

> "You should know the size," she exclaimed. "Wilbur buys all his clothes here!"

Food
Fun

"Forty-eight hamburgers, please," the boy said to the clerk at the roadside stand.

"All for *you*?" gasped the clerk.

"Don't be silly," said the boy, "I have three friends waiting outside for me."

● YOUNG HOUSEWIFE: "Is this milk fresh?"
GROCER: "Fresh? Why, three hours ago it was grass."

Why is it that you cannot starve in the Sahara Desert?

Because of all the sand which is there!

●

DINER: "Do you serve crabs here?"
WAITER: "We serve anyone; sit right down."

●

"This butter is so strong it could walk around the table and say hello to the coffee," said one diner to another in a restaurant.

"Well, if it does the coffee is too weak to talk back."

●

BRIDE: "The two best things I cook are meat loaf and apple dumplings."
GROOM: "Well, which is this?"

●

What has four wheels and flies?

A garbage wagon.

●

DINER in restaurant: "What's this leathery stuff?"
WAITER: "Why, that's filet of sole, sir."
DINER: "How about a nice tender piece from the upper part of the shoe?"

●

MRS. NAG: "I've got my husband to the point where he eats out of my hand."
MRS. GAG: "Saves a lot of dishwashing, doesn't it?"

BROKE: "Do you charge for bread?"
WAITER: "No."
BROKE: "Do you charge for gravy?"
WAITER: "No."
BROKE: "I'll take bread and gravy."

•

MOTHER: "Now Georgie, don't you know you are not supposed to eat with your knife?"
GEORGIE: "I know, Mother, but my fork leaks!"

•

What is the difference between a hungry man and a glutton?

One eats to live, the other lives to eat.

•

An out-of-town visitor went into a café and ordered breakfast. "Please bring me orange juice, two scrambled eggs, toast, and black coffee," he told the waitress. In a minute the waitress returned and said, "What do you mean by 'black coffee'?"

"Without cream or sugar."

"Oh," said the waitress, "we're out of cream—but we *can* serve it without condensed milk."

•

PAUL, in a restaurant: "Go see if the chef has pigs' feet."
SAUL: "I can't tell. He's got his shoes on."

81

What is the best butter in the world?
>*A goat.*

•

What has teeth and never eats?
>*A comb.*

•

JILL: "What kind of fish are they?"
BILL: "Jellyfish."
JILL: "What flavor?"

•

A peanut sat on a railroad track;
His heart was all a-flutter.
A train came speeding down the track.
Toot! Toot! Peanut butter.

•

PAUL: "With which hand do you stir your coffee?"
SAUL: "My right, of course."
PAUL: "*I* use a spoon!"

•

What aunt always provides a place for you to eat?
>*Restaurant.*

•

WAITER: "You ought to have some of our enthusiastic stew."
DINER: "Why do you call it that?"
WAITER: "Because the cook puts everything he has into it."

Taken to the dentist for a checkup, young Jimmy was told he'd have to have a filling.

"Now, Jimmy," asked the dentist, "what kind of filling would you like for that tooth?"

"Chocolate, please," replied Jimmy promptly.

●

What most resembles half a cheese?

The other half.

●

What is it that stays hot even if you put it in a refrigerator?

Pepper.

●

How can you change a pumpkin into another vegetable?

Throw it up into the air and it will come down squash.

●

If eight eggs cost twenty-six cents, how many eggs can you buy for a cent and a quarter?

Eight eggs.

●

What do ghosts eat for breakfast?

Ghost toasties and evaporated milk.

●

DINER: "Hey, Chef! This soup is spoiled."
CHEF: "Yeah, who told you?"
DINER: "A little swallow."

CUSTOMER: "That chicken I bought yesterday had no wish-bone."
BUTCHER, smoothly: "It was a happy and contented chicken, madam, and had nothing to wish for."

●

VISITOR: "Why is your dog watching me so intently while I eat?"
HOST: "Maybe it's because you're eating out of his plate."

Job Jests

SALESMAN: "Sonny, is your mother at home?"

LITTLE SAMMY: "Yes, sir."

SALESMAN (after knocking for some time and getting no answer): "I thought you said she was at home?"

LITTLE SAMMY: "Yes, sir, but I don't live here."

85

MINE FOREMAN: "How come you're carrying only one bag of coal at a time, while the other workers are carrying two?"

MINE WORKER: "Oh, that's because the others are too lazy to make two trips, like *I* do."

•

CASTING DIRECTOR: "That fellow wants a hundred dollars just to play the part of an Indian in the movie."

PRODUCER: "Why, that part is only worth fifty dollars. He's supposed to be a half-breed."

•

PAYMASTER: "How long have you been working here?"

OFFICE BOY: "Ever since the day the boss threatened to fire me."

•

Simpson suddenly became ill and was rushed to the hospital. His boss was among the first to visit him. "My dear George," said the boss soothingly, "don't worry about a thing. Everyone at the office is going to pitch in and do your work—as soon as we can find out what you have been doing."

•

COMEDIAN: "Look here, I do object to going on right after the monkey act."

MANAGER: "You're right. They may think it's an encore."

CHUCK: "Joe sure isn't afraid of work."

CHARLIE: "What makes you think so. I think he is real lazy."

CHUCK: "He can lie down beside work and fall fast asleep."

●

EMPLOYER: "Why were you late this morning?"

OFFICE BOY: "On account of my alarm clock. Everybody in the house got up except me."

EMPLOYER: "How was that?"

OFFICE BOY: "There are nine of us and the alarm clock was only set for eight."

●

The world is full of willing people: some willing to work, the rest willing to let them.

●

EMPLOYER: "I want a responsible boy for this job."

DOPEY: "Then I'm just the right person for you! In every place I ever worked, something went wrong and I was responsible!"

●

PERSONNEL MANAGER to a job hunter: "How old are you?"

> "Eighteen," answered the young man.
>
> "Well, what do you expect to be in, say, three years?"
>
> "Twenty-one," the young man replied without hesitation.

A social worker met one of her charges on the street one very hot day.

SOCIAL WORKER: "What is your brother doing these days, Joe?"

JOE: "Selling snow shovels."

SOCIAL WORKER: "Snow shovels in summer? What's the idea?"

JOE: "Yeah. He figured there would be no competition."

●

PARKER: "Don't you ever take a vacation?"

BARKER: "I can't get away."

PARKER: "Why? Can't the firm do without you?"

BARKER: "And how! That's what I don't want them to find out."

●

HARRY: "Why aren't you working?"

LARRY: "The boss and I had a fight and he won't take back what he said."

HARRY: "What'd he say?"

LARRY: "He said, 'You're fired.'"

●

LENNY: "My father makes faces all day."

BENNY: "Why does he do that?"

LENNY: "Because he works in a clock factory."

●

Did you ever hear about the farmer who crossed his bees with lightning bugs so they could work at night?

MAN: "I read your ad for a man to retail canaries."

BIRD SHOP OWNER: "Yes, do you want the job?"

MAN: "No, I'm just curious as to how the birds lost their tails."

•

IRRITATED EMPLOYER: "*Where* have you been, this last hour?"

INNOCENT EMPLOYEE: "Out having my hair cut."

IRRITATED EMPLOYER: "Well! You can't have your hair cut on *my* time!"

INNOCENT EMPLOYEE: "And why not? It *grew* on your time!"

•

EMPLOYER, on pay day: "Here, Jones, is your pay—for loafing seven hours."

JONES, coolly: "Excuse me—*eight* hours."

•

A girl applied for a job as a stenographer and they gave her a test in spelling.

"How do you spell Mississippi?" she was asked.

"The river or the state?"

•

PATIENT: "What do you charge for extracting a tooth?"

DENTIST: "Five dollars."

PATIENT: "What! For only two seconds' work?"

DENTIST: "Well, if you wish, I can extract it very slowly."

BRIDE, to her neighbor: "You should meet my husband. He makes his living with his pen."
NEIGHBOR, impressed: "You don't say! You mean he's a writer?"
BRIDE: "No, he raises pigs."

●

WARDEN: "Boys, I've had charge of this prison for ten years and we ought to celebrate the occasion. What kind of a party would you suggest?"
PRISONERS, in a chorus: "Open house!"

●

CIRCUS OWNER: "Are you the famous lion tamer—the great Flambino?"
JOB APPLICANT: "No, I only comb the lions and clean their teeth."

Money Mumbles

Walking along a street a man was attracted by frightened screams from a house. Rushing in he found a mother frantic because her little son had swallowed a quarter. Seizing the child by the heels, he held him up, gave him a few shakes, and the coin dropped to the floor. The grateful mother was lost in admiration.

"You certainly knew how to get it out of him," she said. "Are you a doctor?"

"No, madam," the man replied, "I'm from the Internal Revenue Bureau."

SHOPPER: "How much are these tomatoes?"

GROCER: "Forty cents a pound."

SHOPPER: "Did you raise them yourself?"

GROCER: "Yes, ma'am, I certainly did. They were only thirty-five cents yesterday."

•

DOPE: "Would you sooner lose your life, or your money?"

DOPIER: "Why, my life, of course. I'll need my money for my old age."

•

A touring American businessman noticed an Indian chief lolling at the door of his wigwam on the reservation.

"Chief," suggested the tourist, "why don't you get a job in a factory?"

"Why?" grunted the chief.

"Well, you could earn a lot of money. Maybe thirty or forty dollars a week."

"Why?" insisted the chief.

"Oh, if you worked hard and saved your money, you'd soon have a bank account. Wouldn't you like that?"

"Why?" again asked the chief.

"I'll tell you," shouted the tourist. "With a bank account you could retire, and then you wouldn't have to work any more."

"Not working now," pointed out the chief.

For many minutes there had been a violent ringing at the night bell of a drug store until finally the druggist, who lived above it, sleepily crawled into his clothes and went downstairs. A kilted Scotsman stood in front of the store.

"Five cents' worth o' bicarbonate of soda for indigestion, if ye please," the Scotsman requested.

"A nickel's worth of bicarbonate of soda at this time of night?" exploded the druggist. "Getting me up for that when a glass of warm water would have done just as well!"

"Weel, weel," returned the Scot, putting his money back in his pocket. "I thank ye for the advice, and I'll no' bother ye after all. Good night."

●

"Just tell me one good reason *why* you can't buy a new car now," said the persistent automobile salesman.

"Well, I'll tell you, sir," replied the farmer, "I'm still paying installments on the car I swapped for the car I traded in as part payment on the car I own now."

●

PAUL: "Could you loan me ten dollars?"
JOE: "I hate to do it, because when a fellow lends money it always breaks up a friendship."
PAUL: "Oh, come now! We haven't been *such* good friends."

A woman was trying to collect compensation for an accident. When the adjuster for the company called, she demanded loudly, "I want $20,000 for that lost thumb."

"But madam, that seems a lot of money for just a thumb."

"Well, it isn't," she insisted. "It's the one I kept my husband under."

•

"You know, I think everyone should divide his worldly goods with the other fellow," said one office worker to another.

"That's a good idea. If you had two thousand dollars, would you give me one half?"
"Sure."
"And if you had two automobiles, would you give me one?"
"Sure."
"And if you had two shirts, would you give me one?"
"No."
"Why?"
"Because I've *got* two shirts."

•

WOMAN SHOPPER at the counter: "I suspect that you're giving me awfully short weight for my money!"
BUTCHER: "Well, I'm positive you're giving me an awful long wait for mine."

 94

What did the adding machine say to the clerk?
You can count on me.

•

A business man from Texas who was a visitor in New York stood watching a building being constructed. After an hour or so, he noticed a rough-dressed man also standing by, also watching, and smoking one cigar after another. Finally he said,

"How many cigars do you smoke a day?"

"About ten," the man answered.

"What do they cost you?"

"Twenty-five cents apiece."

"My, that's two dollars and a half a day! How long have you been smoking?"

"Thirty years."

"Two-fifty a day for thirty years is a lot of money."

"Yes, it is."

"Do you see that office building on the corner?"

"Yes."

"If you had never smoked in your life you might *own* that fine building."

The man took the cigar out of his mouth, looked squarely at his questioner and said, "Do *you* smoke?"

"No, never did."

"Do you own that building?"

"No."

"Well, I *do*."

95

VISITING UNCLE: "If you're real good, Johnnie, I'll give you this bright new penny."
JOHNNIE: "Haven't you got a dirty old quarter?"

●

FRANK: "What do you find the most difficult thing on the piano?"
HANK: "To pay the installments."

●

JUDGE: "Now tell me, why did you steal that purse?"
PRISONER: "Your honor, I was not feeling well and I thought the change would do me good."

●

Two young men were discussing matrimony.

"You wouldn't marry a girl just for her money, would you?"

"No," said the other fellow, "but I wouldn't have the heart to let her die an old maid just because she had money, either."

Meet *these* Menaces

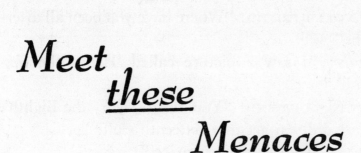

VISITOR: "And what will you do, dear, when you are as big as your mother?"

LITTLE GIRL: "Diet."

IMPATIENT FRIEND: "Where have you been all after-noon?"

DOPEY: "I saw a picture called 'Henry the Six-teenth'."

IMPATIENT FRIEND: "You mean 'Henry the Eighth'. Where did you get that sixteenth stuff?"

DOPEY: "I sat through it twice."

•

Little Polly counted her chestnuts carefully and then approached her grandma.

"Grammaw, can you eat nuts?" she asked.

"No, dear, I have no teeth," Grandma replied. Little Polly emptied her apron into grandma's lap, saying, "Then you can mind these till I come back from school."

•

SILLY: "I'm going to join a circus."

BILLY: "What are you going to do in a circus?"

SILLY: "I'm going to be a midget."

BILLY: "You're too big for a midget."

SILLY: "That's the idea. I'll be the biggest midget in the world."

•

JOE: "Say, Dad, that apple I just ate had a worm in it, and I ate that, too."

DAD: "What! Here, drink this water and wash it down."

JOE (shaking his head): "Naw, let 'im *walk* down!"

JOHN, JR.: "Hey, Pop—*that* man wasn't a painless dentist like he advertised."

POP: "Why? Did he hurt you?"

JOHN, JR.: "No, but he yelled when I bit his thumb, just like any other dentist."

•

BENJIE: "Mom, do you remember that vase you always worried I would break?"

MOM: "Yes, what about it?"

BENJIE: "Your worries are over."

•

HARRY: "A steam roller ran over my uncle."

LARRY: "What did you do?"

HARRY: "I just took him home and slipped him under the door."

PAUL: "See that house? That's where Uncle Tom lived."

SAUL: "Uncle Tom from 'Uncle Tom's Cabin'?"

PAUL: "Yes."

SAUL: "Never even heard of him."

●

LENNY: "What is that you're chewing?"

BENNY: "It's called 'Magic Gum'—the more you chew it, the smarter you get. I'm going to chew this piece second and have a lot of swell ideas."

LENNY: "Got any more?"

BENNY: "I've only got one stick left. I'll sell it to you for ten dollars."

LENNY: "Here's the ten dollars."

BENNY: "Here's the gum."

LENNY: "Boy, it's all right. It tastes good. Do you think I'll get smart from this? Funny. I don't feel any different. I think it's a joke."

BENNY: "Say, you're smart already!"

●

DOPEY: "My father can hold up an auto with one hand."

DOPIER: "He must be very strong."

DOPEY: "No, he's a cop."

●

TEACHER: "Give for one year the number of tons of coal shipped out of the United States."

TED: "In fourteen-hundred-ninety-two—none."

TOMMY: "I always do a good deed every day."
SUNDAY SCHOOL TEACHER: "That's fine—what good deed have you done today?"
TOMMY: "Why, there was only castor oil enough for one of us this morning, so I let my little brother have it."

●

A club of eccentric young college boys had for one of their rules that on Monday evenings any man in the clubroom who asked a question which he was unable to answer himself should pay a fine of one dollar. One evening Parker asked, "Why doesn't a ground squirrel leave any dirt around the top of his hole when he digs it?"

After some deliberation he was called upon to answer his own question.

"That's easy," he said. "The squirrel starts at the bottom and digs up."

"All very nice," suggested a member, "but how does it get to the bottom?"

"That's *your* question," answered Parker.

●

"Lady, could you give me a quarter so I can get to see my family?" asked the ragged little boy.

"Certainly, my boy," said the generous lady, as she handed the coin to him. "And where is your family?"

"At the movies," he answered, as he ran off.

RANDY: "Do you have any bloodhounds?"

ANDY: "Yes. Come here, Pooch."

RANDY: "But he doesn't look like a bloodhound to me."

ANDY: "Bleed for the lady, Pooch!"

•

Gerald was going to have a birthday party, and his mother insisted on his inviting, among others, a neighbor's boy with whom he had had a fight. He finally promised to do so, but on the day of the party the neighbor's boy failed to turn up.

Walter's mother became suspicious. "Did you invite George?" she asked, after the party.

"Of course I did, Mother. I not only invited him to come, I *dared* him to."

Lady at the Wheel

"I turned the way I signaled," said the lady indignantly, after the crash.

"I know it," retorted the man she'd hit. "That's what fooled me."

TRAFFIC OFFICER: "Now tell me, just what could the other driver have done to avoid this accident?"
WOMAN DRIVER, indignantly: "He could have gone down another street!"

●

The woman auto tourist posed for a snapshot in front of the fallen pillars of an ancient temple in Rome.

"Don't get the car in the picture," she pleaded, "or my husband will think I ran into the place!"

●

A woman driver was sailing along a country road when she noticed a couple of repair men climbing telephone poles.

"Dopes!" she exclaimed to her companion, "they must think I never drove a car before."

●

A woman driving in Chicago stopped her car for a red light. However, when the light turned green again, she just stayed right where she was. When the light had changed several times and she still hadn't moved, the traffic policeman finally went over and inquired politely, "Lady, ain't we got no colors you like?"

●

TRAFFIC COP: "Miss, you were doing seventy miles an hour!"
SWEET YOUNG THING: "Oh, isn't that splendid! And I only just learned to drive yesterday."

Bob: "Does your mother know much about cars?"
Rob: "Naw. She thinks you cool the motor by stripping the gears."

•

Visiting friend: "Oh, Mabel, I do wish *I* could afford a car like this!"
Mabel: "So do *I*!"

•

George: "Is your wife having any better luck in learning to drive the car?"
Jim: "Well, the road is beginning to turn when she does."

•

The examiner was testing an applicant for a driver's license.

"What does it mean," he asked, "when a woman is holding out her hand?"

"It means," answered the applicant, "she's turning left, turning right, backing up, waving at somebody, or going to stop."

•

A woman drove a Ford into a service station to complain that her car was using too much gas. The attendant pointed to the choke which protruded from the dashboard: "Do you know what *this* is for?" he asked.

"Oh, *that* gadget," replied the woman airily. "I never use it, so I keep it pulled out to hang my handbag on."

POLICEMAN: "Don't you know that you should always give over half of the road to a woman driver?"
TIMID MALE DRIVER: "I always do—when I find out which half she wants."

COP: "What ya mean, goin' seventy miles an hour?"
PRETTY MOTORIST: "My brakes don't work and I was hustling to get home before I had an accident."

POLICEMAN: "How did you knock him down?"
LADY DRIVER: "I didn't! I stopped to let him go across, and he fainted!"

 106

Oh, Doctor!

"Did you go to another doctor before you came to me?" asked the doctor.

"No," replied the patient, "I went to a druggist."

"And what foolish advice did *he* give you?"

"He told me to come to you," said the patient.

PHYSICIAN: "Shall I give your wife a local anesthetic?"

WEALTHY HUSBAND: "No. I'm rich—give her the best! Give her something imported."

●

Mrs. Peterson complained to her doctor that his bill was too high.

"Don't forget," the doctor reminded her, "that I made eleven visits to Johnny when he had the measles."

"And don't *you* forget," she replied, "that Johnny made you lots of money by giving the measles to the whole fourth grade!"

●

DOCTOR: "I don't like the looks of your husband."

WIFE: "I don't either, but he is good to the children."

●

LADY (standing in the middle of a busy street): "Officer, can you tell me how to get to the hospital?"

POLICEMAN: "Just stand where you are."

●

The famous surgeon and his wife were in their library.

"Robert," his wife exclaimed, "why did you tear the back part out of my new book?"

"Excuse me, dear," he answered, "the part you speak of was labeled 'appendix' and I took it out without thinking."

"Your pulse is as steady as a clock," announced the doctor to the worried patient.

"Well, but you've got your hand on my wrist watch," he replied.

●

DOCTOR: "What do you dream about at night?"

DOPEY: "Baseball."

DOCTOR: "Don't you dream about anything else?"

DOPEY: "No, just about baseball, night after night."

DOCTOR (puzzled): "Don't you ever dream about food?"

DOPEY: "What? And miss my turn at bat?"

●

DOCTOR: "How is your wife getting along with her reducing diet?"

MR. SMALL: "Fine. She disappeared last week."

●

PAUL: "What does he do for a living?"

SAUL: "He used to be a surgeon, but he had to quit."

PAUL: "Too hard on his nerves?"

SAUL: "No, too much inside work."

●

HOUSEWIFE: "Look here, my man, why do you always come to *my* house to beg?"

TRAMP: "Doctor's orders, madam."

HOUSEWIFE: "Doctor's orders?"

TRAMP: "He told me that when I found food that agreed with me I should stick to it."

109

"Doctor," said a patient, "it is mighty nice of you to come all this distance to see me."

"Oh, that's all right," said the doctor. "You see, I have another patient in this section so I thought I would just kill two birds with one stone."

●

DANNY: "Do you know what a vegetarian is?"

DOPEY: "Sure, a horse doctor."

DANNY: "No. That's a veterinarian."

DOPEY: "Oh, I thought a veterinarian was a soldier."

●

FUSSY LADY PATIENT: "Do you think raw oysters are healthy?"

WEARY DOCTOR: "I never knew one to complain."

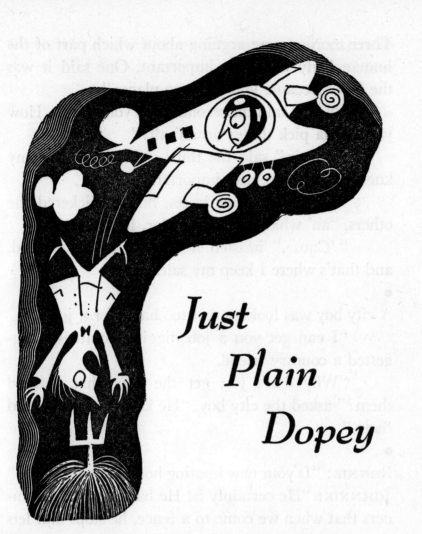

Just Plain Dopey

Once there were two men riding in an airplane.
Unfortunately, one fell out.
Fortunately, there was a haystack below him.
Unfortunately, there was a pitchfork in the haystack.
Fortunately, he missed the pitchfork.
Unfortunately, he missed the haystack.

III

Three morons were arguing about which part of the human body was most important. One said it was the feet, "because yuh gotta go places."

"Naw," said the second. "It's your hands. How yuh gonna pick things up an' all?"

"No, sir," said the third, "the dimples in my knees—*that's* the most important part."

"Dimples in your knees, huh?" snickered the others, "an' whatcha say that for, huh?"

" 'Cause," insisted he, "I eat celery in bed, and that's where I keep my salt."

●

A city boy was looking, not too hard, for a job.

"I can get you a job digging potatoes," suggested a country friend.

"Why don't you get the man that planted them?" asked the city boy. "He knows where he hid them."

●

RONNIE: "Is your new hunting horse well-behaved?"
JOHNNIE: "He certainly is! He has such good manners that when we come to a fence, he stops and lets me go over first."

●

A handyman doing a hauling job was told that he couldn't get his pay until he made out a statement. After much thought, he handed in the following bill: "Ten comes and ten goes, at four bits a went, $10."

In the bank one day the little moron suddenly called out at the top of his voice, "Did anyone drop a roll of bills with a rubber band around it?"
Several people at different tellers' windows answered, "I did!"

"Well, I just now found the rubber band," said the little moron.

•

HARRY: "Here comes the parade now. Mary'll miss it if she doesn't come to the window. Where is she?"
CARRIE: "She's upstairs waving her hair."
HARRY: "For Pete's sake, hasn't she got a flag?"

•

FIRST MORON: "Are you crazy if you talk to yourself?"
SECOND MORON: "No, but you are if you listen."

•

CITY MORON: "Why does cream cost more than milk?"
COUNTRY MORON: "Because it's harder for the cows to sit on the small bottles."

A farmer was driving past an insane asylum with a load of fertilizer. An inmate of the asylum saw him and called, "What are you hauling?"

"Fertilizer," the farmer replied.

"What are you going to do with it?"

"Put it on strawberries."

"You ought to live in here; *we* get sugar and cream on them."

●

MECHANIC: "Have we any four-volt, two-watt bulbs?"
HELPER: "For what?"
MECHANIC: "No, two."
HELPER: "Two what?"
MECHANIC: "Yes."

●

SAM: "Joe, did you know that a cat has three tails?"
JOE: "Don't be silly."
SAM: "But I can prove it."
JOE: "Try it."
SAM: "Well, you'll have to agree that no cat has two tails."
JOE: "Right."
SAM: "And one cat has one more tail than no cat, hasn't it?"
JOE: "Of course."
SAM: "So, one cat has three tails."

CITY MORON: "Why does the cream rise to the top of the milk?"

COUNTRY MORON: "So the people can get it."

•

Two morons were gossiping. "Cal," said one, "tell me something. Is Mr. Oglethorpe worth any money?"

"I don't know what he's worth, but he saves fifty dollars a day."

"How does he save fifty dollars a day?"

"He goes in the post office every day and there's a big sign there—fifty-dollar fine for spitting —so he don't spit."

•

A country moron was on a trip to the big city. He went into a drug store to telephone a friend. There he saw a dial phone for the first time. He looked at it, studied it, looked at it again, then came out.

"I've got to get to another telephone," he said to his brother.

"Why, what's the matter with the telephone in there?"

"It's got holes in it."

•

TV FAN: "What's that you've got?"

MECHANIC: "An invention I'm making for a television set."

TV FAN: "What is it?"

MECHANIC: "A combination of nuts and wisecracks."

115

Did you hear the one about the moron who backed off the bus because he heard a lady say she was going to grab his seat as soon as he got up?

•

COXSWAIN: "How is your insomnia?"
SHIP'S COOK: "I'm getting worse. I can't even sleep when it's time to get up."

•

Why did the moron tiptoe past the medicine chest?
> *He didn't want to wake the sleeping pills.*

•

A man got off a train at Albuquerque, New Mexico.
> "I beg your pardon," he said to an Indian, "what's your name?"
> "Me Running Deer."
> "Is that your son there?"
> "Yes."
> "What's his name?"
> "Ninety-eight Cents."
> "Why do you call him Ninety-eight Cents?"
> "Because he's no buck yet."

•

CUSTOMER: "I understand this is a second-hand store."
CLERK: "Yes, it is."
CUSTOMER: "Well, then, I want one for my watch."

😊 116

The plane for Chicago was well on its way, when the pilot began to laugh hilariously.

PASSENGER: "What's the joke?"

PILOT: "I'm thinking of what they'll say at the asylum when they find out I have escaped."

•

Good old Dr. Make-you-well was trying to sell young Bobby the idea of including a few vegetables in his daily diet.

"Carrots," he said, "*that's* the ticket. They're good for your eyes."

"I don't believe that baloney," stated Bobby firmly.

"Well, did you ever see a rabbit with glasses?" asked the doctor.

•

A nurse noticed a mental patient with his ear close to the wall listening intently. Holding up a warning finger to be quiet, he beckoned the nurse closer and said, "Listen here." The nurse listened for some time and then said, "*I* can't hear anything."

"No," said the patient, "and it's been like that all day."

A be-bop bystander watching a goat who had fallen into a whirling cement mixer said, "Man, look at that crazy mixed-up kid!"

●

DOPEY: "Since you do not have any speedometer on your flivver, how do you tell how fast you are going?"

DOPIER: "That's simple; when I go ten miles an hour my tail light rattles; when I go twenty miles an hour my fenders rattle; when I go forty miles an hour my teeth rattle; when I go fifty miles an hour my bones rattle."

DOPEY: "What happens when you go sixty miles an hour?"

DOPIER: "I don't know, but I *think* I go to heaven."

Ouch!

"Yes," said the boastful young man, "my family can trace its ancestry back to the *Mayflower*."

"I suppose," remarked his friend, sarcastically, "next you'll be telling us that your ancestors were in the Ark with Noah?"

"Certainly not," said the other. "*My* people had a boat of their own."

SALLY: "I dreamed last night that I had invented a new type of breakfast food and was sampling it when—"

MOLLY: "Yes, yes, go on."

SALLY: "—then I woke up and found a corner of the mattress gone!"

●

VALET: "Sir, your car is at the door."

MASTER: "Yes. I can hear it knocking."

●

VISITING FRIEND: "Are the girls in this town pretty?"

HIS HOST: "Well, let me put it this way—we held a beauty contest and nobody won."

●

TEACHER: "Can anyone here tell me some of the uses of cowhide?"

PUPIL: "Well, it helps keep the cow together!"

●

BEN: "One of our little pigs was sick so I gave him some sugar."

DAN: "Sugar! What for?"

BEN: "Haven't you ever heard of sugar-cured ham?"

●

IRRITATED MAN, to the telephone operator: "Why *can't* you get me the zoo?"

OPERATOR, in a cool voice: "Because the lion is busy!"

A jeweler was taking a grandfather clock to his shop for repairs. On his way in a crowded street, he bumped into a lady and accidentally knocked several bundles from her arms.

"Why can't you be like other people," bellowed the infuriated lady, "and just wear a watch?"

•

DEAN: "Old Mr. Fussbudget flunked out of our school forty years ago and now he has died and left us a million dollars."

MRS. DEAN: "Ah, a very forgiving spirit."

DEAN: "I'm not so sure. The gift has a rather peculiar condition—it is to be used only for paying the transportation of students transferring to other institutions of learning."

•

FANNIE: "Are you going to take the car out in this rainstorm?"

DANNIE: "Certainly. It's a driving rain, isn't it?"

An immigrant, taking his test for naturalization papers, was asked, "Who is the president of the United States?"

"Eisenhower," he answered.

"Could *you* be president?" was the next question he was asked.

"No."

Nodding encouragingly, the questioner asked, "Why not?"

"I'm too busy right now," explained the immigrant gently.

•

Two eagles were lazily soaring over the desert when a jet-propelled plane sped by them, its exhaust spouting flame and smoke. As it went out of sight, one of the eagles remarked:

"That bird was really in a hurry."

"You'd be in a hurry too," said the other, "if *your* tail was on fire."

•

Why is a watermelon filled with water?

Because it's planted in the spring.

•

The little moron took a friend driving in the mountains. After a while his friend said, "Every time you race around one of those sharp curves, I get scared!"

"Then why don't you do what *I* do?" the little moron suggested. "Close your eyes."

MOTHER: "Have you filled the salt shakers?"
BETTY: "Not yet, Mother. It's hard pushing the salt through these little holes!"

●

A preacher dialed long distance to put a call through to a clergyman in a faraway town.

"Do you wish to place a station-to-station call?" asked the operator.

"No," he said. "Make it parson-to-parson."

●

TEACHER: "What was George Washington noted for?"
RUSTY: "His memory."
TEACHER: "What makes you think his memory was so great?"
RUSTY: "Because they erected a monument to Washington's memory."

BOSS: "Simpson, what are you doing with your feet on the desk?"
SIMPSON: "Economy, sir—my eraser wore out, so I'm using my rubber heels."

A huge elephant and a tiny mouse were in the same cage at the zoo. The elephant looked down at the mouse nastily and trumpeted in disgust, "You're the puniest, the weakest, the most insignificant thing I've ever seen!"

"Well," piped the mouse in a plaintive squeak, "don't forget, I've been sick."

•

An employer said to a man applying for a job: "You ask high wages for a man with no experience."
"Well," the prospect replied, "it's so much harder work when you don't know anything about it."

•

FIRST LADY: "My sister's baby swallowed a bottle of ink!"
SECOND LADY: "Incredible!"
FIRST LADY: "No. Indelible."

•

PAUL: "Your new overcoat is pretty loud, isn't it?"
SAUL: "Yeah, but I'm gonna buy a muffler to go with it."

FIRST WORKMAN (getting on bus): "It's going to be tough sleddin' today."
SECOND WORKMAN: "Why do you say that?"
FIRST WORKMAN: "Because there's no snow!"

•

PROUD MOTHER: "Yes, he's fourteen months old now and he's been walking since he was eight months old!"
BORED VISITOR: "Really? He must be awfully tired."

•

POLLY: "How did Santa Claus treat you?"
MOLLY: "He brought me this lovely woolen sweater."
POLLY: "That isn't wool. It's plainly marked 'cotton'."
MOLLY: "Yes, I know—that's to fool the moths."

•

Mrs. Newlywed was eager to prove to her husband what a good cook she was, and on the servant's day off, set about cooking a chicken for his dinner. She plucked the fowl carefully, arranged it neatly in a pot, and put it in the oven.

Two hours later she heard a loud banging on the oven door. She opened the door to find the chicken looking up at her piteously.

"Lady," it cried pleadingly, "either give me back my feathers or turn on the gas. I'm freezing to death in this oven!"

MRS. MORTIMER, to the new maid: "We'll have breakfast promptly at eight o'clock."
MAID: "All right, ma'am. If I'm not down on time, don't wait."

•

STRANGER: "I was born in South America."
NATIVE: "What part?"
STRANGER: "All of me, of course."

•

NEIGHBOR: "Where's your brother, Johnny?"
JOHNNY: "In the house playing a duet. I finished my part first."

•

"Wilt thou give me the pleasure of accompanying me in a game of croquet?" spake Sir Gawain.
"Nay, nay, I dast not,"
quoth the shy Lady Elinor.
" 'Tis a wicket game."

Ouch Again!

A man dropped in to pay a friend an unexpected visit, and was amazed to find him playing chess with his dog. The man watched in silence for a few minutes, then burst out with: "That's the smartest dog I ever saw in my life!"

"Oh, he isn't so smart," was the answer. "I've beaten him three games out of four!"

127

When the clock strikes 13, what time is it?

Time to get it fixed.

●

DOOPEY: "I hope the rain keeps up."

LOOPEY: "Why?"

DOOPEY: "So it won't come down."

●

"Mother," said the baby moth, "I just found a tiny moth crying."

Mother answered, "Who ever heard of a moth crying?"

"Oh, Mommy," said the baby moth, "haven't you ever seen a moth ball?"

●

A lady went into a store and asked, "May I try on that dress in the window?"

"Well—" said the new clerk doubtfully. "Don't you think it would be better to use the dressing room?"

●

Why are fishermen so stingy?

Because their business makes them sell fish (selfish).

●

BILL: "I wish you boys wouldn't call me Big Bill."

PHIL: "Why not?"

BILL: "Those college names stick—and I'm going to be a doctor."

DOPEY: "If *I* had a thousand men, and *you* had a thousand men, and we had a war, who would win?"
DOPIER: "I give up."
DOPEY: "*I* win! You just gave up!"

•

PAUL: "What is the best way to make a coat last?"
SAUL: "Make the vest and trousers first!"

•

GOLF STUDENT: "Well, how do you like my game?"
PRO: "I suppose it's all right, but I still prefer golf."

•

Why is a pair of skates like an apple?

> *They both have to do with the fall of man.*

•

The telephone bell on a prominent economist's desk rang insistently. When he answered, a voice informed him,

"You're all wet about the cost of living reaching a new high! My wife and I live sumptuously—eating everything we like—on sixty-eight cents a week."

"Sixty-eight cents a week!" echoed the economist. "I can't believe it! Won't you tell me how? And to make sure I get the story straight, please speak louder."

"I *can't* speak louder," came the answer. "I'm a goldfish."

FIRST PELICAN: "That's fine fish you have there."
SECOND PELICAN: "Well, it fills the bill."

•

PAUL: "I saw a fellow strike a girl today."
SAUL: "You didn't let him get away with it, did you?"
PAUL: "I went up to him and said, 'Only a coward would hit a woman—why don't you hit a man?'"
SAUL: "Then what happened?"
PAUL: "That's all I remember."

Ouch! Ouch! Ouch!

"Herbert," said a mother to her six-year-old son, "are you teaching the parrot to use slang after I asked you not to?"

"No, Mama," replied Herbert. "I was just telling him what not to say."

131

Two voices were heard in the park one beautiful evening.

"I love you," said one.

"Ouch!" yelled the other.

"I love you."

"Ouch!"

It was two porcupines necking.

●

When is it easy to read in the woods?

When autumn turns the leaves.

●

Could you light a candle if you had a box of candles and no matches?

Just take a candle out of the box and you will make the box a candle lighter.

●

How many balls of string would it take to reach the moon?

Only one—if it were long enough.

●

PAUL: "Why Saul, where did you get that nice Easter tie?"

SAUL: "What makes you think it's an Easter tie?"

PAUL: "It's got egg on it."

●

How do sailors get their clothes clean?

They throw them overboard and they are washed ashore.

BRAGGY: "Where I come from they do things in a hurry. Why, they put up buildings quicker than in any other city. They start a twenty-story building one day and in a week it's finished."

BRAGGIER: "That's nothing—you should come down to our town. I was going to work one morning and they were laying the cornerstone of a building. When I came home from work that night, the landlord was putting tenants out for not paying their rent."

●

WILLIS: "Why do you comb your hair before going to bed?"

PHYLLIS: "To make a good impression on the pillow."

●

Why is a locomotive like a stick of gum?

> *One goes choo choo, the other goes chew chew.*

●

DAN: "In a couple of years you will all have to look up to me."

NAN: "How's that?"

DAN: "I'm going to be a window cleaner."

●

PHIL: "Didn't I tell you about Mrs. Spitz? She had triplets and two weeks later she had twins."

BILL: "That's impossible. How did it happen?"

PHIL: "Well, one of the triplets got lost."

MOPEY: "My hair is getting thin."
DOPEY: "Well, who wants fat hair?"

●

DONNIE: "Isn't nature wonderful?"
CONNIE: "Why do you say that?"
DONNIE: "Well, thousands of years ago she didn't know man was going to invent glasses, yet look how conveniently she placed his ears!"

●

You tell 'em, mountain . . . I'm only a bluff!

●

MR. MEEK, to the barber: "My hair is coming out—what can I get to keep it in?"
BARBER: "A paper bag."

●

PAUL: "I saw something last night I'll never get over."
MOLL: "What was that?"
PAUL: "The moon."

Lilliputian Logic

Dorothy, aged six, was watching her mother put cold cream on her face.

"What's that for, Mummy," she asked.

"It's face cream, dear, to make me beautiful."
A little while later, after the cold cream had been wiped off, Dorothy looked at her mother for a minute, shook her head, and remarked sadly, "Didn't work, did it, Mummy?"

Five-year-old Bettina was getting ready for bed. Suddenly she turned to her mother and asked, "Mother, are we going to move tomorrow?"

"Yes, dear, this is the last night you will sleep here."

"Then," said Bettina, kneeling beside her bed, "I'd better say good-by to God now if we're moving to Cleveland in the morning."

•

Little Victoria, watching the farm hands spreading out a stack of hay to dry, could contain her curiosity no longer, so she politely asked, "Is it a needle you're looking for?"

•

Hostess (at a children's birthday party): "Jackie, does your mother allow you to have two pieces of cake when you are at home?"

Jackie (who has just asked for a second piece): "No, ma'am."

Hostess: "Well, do you think she'd like you to have two pieces here?"

Jackie, confidentially: "Oh, *she* wouldn't care. This isn't *her* cake!"

•

A little boy who had been used to receiving his older brother's old toys and clothes recently remarked,

"Mom, will I have to marry his widow when he dies?"

😃 136

Three-year-old Patty's mother sent her for a switch to be punished with. Patty was gone quite a while, and when she finally came in her mother asked her for the switch.

Patty sobbed a little and said, "The tree was too big for me to reach, but here's a wock you can fwow at me."

●

Lenny's mother was trying to explain to him that the neighbor's dog was a good dog and wouldn't bite.

"Well, if he did eat me up would I go to heaven like a good boy?" the child asked.

His mother said that of course he would.

"Well, then," the boy said after a moment's thought, "wouldn't that dog have to go too?"

●

"Look, Mother!" cried little Danny, "there's a big bear in the back yard."

"You know perfectly well that's Johnny Jackson's dog. Now go to your room and ask God to forgive you for telling a lie."

In a few minutes Danny was back downstairs.

"Did you ask God to forgive you?" his mother asked.

"Yes, I did," said Danny. "And he said it was all right. God said the first time He saw Johnny Jackson's dog He thought it was a bear Himself!"

"Can any of you children tell me who lived in the Garden of Eden?" asked the Sunday-school teacher.

"Yes, teacher," said a little girl, "I think it was the Adamses."

TEACHER: "Randy, if you put your hand in one pants pocket and you find seventy-five cents and you put your hand in the other pants pocket and you find twenty-five cents, what would you have?"

RANDY, promptly: "I'd have somebody else's pants on!"

Dumb Question,
Dumb Answer

JACK: "Today I saw a baby that gained ten pounds in two weeks by drinking elephant's milk."
MARY: "You don't say! Whose baby was it?"
JACK: "The elephant's."

139

"My father died at sea. My grandfather died at sea. And my great-grandfather died at sea," related the sailor.

"My, my," remarked the visiting sentimental old lady, "if all your ancestors died at sea, how did you *dare* enlist in the navy?"

"Ma'am," responded the sailor, "where did *your* father die?"

"In bed."

"Your grandfather?"

"In bed, too."

"Your great-grandfather?"

"He also died in bed."

"Then," said the seaman, "how do you *dare* go to bed, since all your ancestors died there?"

•

BRIDE: "Harry! Harry! Wake up! I just heard a mouse squeak!"

GROOM, drowsily: "What do you want me to do—get up and oil it?"

•

A court official, after explaining the history of the American flag to a group of aliens seeking citizenship papers, asked one of them, "Tell me—what flies over the City Hall?"

The foreigner thought a moment, then, "Peejins!" he shouted triumphantly.

Mr. and Mrs.

WIFE: "I think you might talk to me while I sew."
HUSBAND: "Why don't you sew to me while I read?"

●

SHE: "Then you'll take me for a drive on Thursday?"
HE: "Yes, but suppose it rains?"
SHE: "Come the day before, then."

She had just received a beautiful skunk coat as a gift from her husband.

SHE: "I can't see how such a nice coat comes from such a foul-smelling beast."

HE: "I don't ask for thanks, dear. But I do think I deserve respect."

•

She came to the police station with a picture in her hand. "My husband has disappeared," she sobbed. "Here is his picture, I want you to find him."

The inspector looked up from the photograph. "Why?" he asked.

•

BOOK-STORE CLERK: "Here's a new book called *How to Help Your Husband Get Ahead*."

BRIDE: "Oh, no thank you. My husband already has one."

•

HUBBY: "What's the matter with this suit I just bought? What don't you like about it? The store said it was a perfect fit."

WIFE: "It looks more like a convulsion."

•

YOUNG WIFE: "I really managed to save something this month. I put a hundred dollars in the bank."

YOUNG HUSBAND: "Wonderful! It wasn't so hard, was it?"

YOUNG WIFE: "It was easy. I just tore up the bills."

What is the difference between a kiss, color television, and a monkey?

> *The kiss is so* dear, *color television is too* dear, *and the monkey is* you, *dear.*

●

SMITH: "Who is your wife going to vote for?"

JONES: "For whoever I vote for."

SMITH: "Who are you going to vote for?"

JONES: "She hasn't decided yet."

●

BRIDEGROOM: "My wife and I have a joint checking account."

BEST FRIEND: "Isn't that hard to keep straight?"

BRIDEGROOM: "No. I put in the money and she takes it out."

●

DOCTOR: "I'm sorry to tell you that your wife's mind is completely gone."

MR. PECK: "I'm not surprised. She's been giving me a piece of it every day for twenty years."

●

WIFE: "Wait a minute—did you shave?"

HUSBAND: "Of course I shaved."

WIFE: "Next time, stand a little closer to the razor."

●

HUSBAND TO WIFE: "Well, in a way, it's a two-week vacation . . . I take a week and then the boss takes a week."

WIFE: "Goodness, Henry, this isn't *our* baby."
HENRY: "Shut up! It's a better buggy!"

●

A multimillionaire, being interviewed about his self-made fortune, said: "I never hesitate to give full credit to my wife for her assistance."

"In what way did she help?" the reporter asked.

"Well, if you want the whole truth," replied the man, "I was curious to find out if there was any income she couldn't live beyond."

●

What sentence of three words which reads the same backward and forward did Adam use when he introduced himself to Eve?

"Madam, I'm Adam."

Bloopers and Blunders

In a midwestern cemetery, this sign appears:
"It is forbidden for any persons to pick
flowers from any but their own graves."

The unfortunate woman was killed while cooking her husband's breakfast in a horrible manner.

News note in a COUNTRY PAPER

●

"Father," said the adoring mother, "Jonathan's teacher says he ought to have an encyclopedia."

"Encyclopedia, my eye," grumbled his father. "Let him *walk* to school, like I did."

●

Columbia, Tennessee, which calls itself the largest outdoor mule market in the world, recently held a mule parade headed by the governor.

NEW YORK MAGAZINE

●

A four-year-old girl was taken to church for the first time, and was very much impressed by it all. And when everyone knelt down, she whispered, "Mummy, what are they doing now?"

"Shhh!" cautioned her mother, "they're getting ready to say their prayers."

"*What?*" yelled the child in amazement, "with all their *clothes on?*"

●

SANDY: "We've got a new baby at our house."
MANDY: "Where did you get it?"
SANDY: "We got it from Doctor Brown."
MANDY: "We take from him, too."

146

What did the big firecracker say to the little fire-cracker?

"My pop is bigger than your pop."

●

BILLY: "I got a new little baby brother."

MILLY: "*Another* one? Gee, you've got about nineteen already, haven't you?"

BILLY: "Yeah."

MILLY: "What's his name?"

BILLY: "We called him Joe for two days."

MILLY: "For two days? Then what happened?"

BILLY: "After two days my father and mother found out we've already *got* a Joe in the family."

●

Little five-year-old Betty was taken to church for the first time. As she walked out of the church with her parents, the preacher stopped her, leaned over, and asked her how she liked church.

"I liked the music okay," said Betty, "but the commercial was too long."

●

A lady decided to have the little neighbor boy stay for lunch one day. As the meal got under way, she watched his struggles to manipulate his knife and fork and, hoping to be helpful, finally asked him,

"Are you sure you can cut your steak?"

"Oh yes," he replied. "We often have it this tough at home."

The visiting governor of Maine was addressing a group of the inmates of a penitentiary.

"Fellow citizens," he began, then stopped short, because they were not citizens.

"Fellow convicts," he began again, then realized he was again off the beam.

"Well, boys," he finally said, "I don't know what to call you, but I'm mighty glad to see so many here."

●

Dr. Carson Carter, noted health authority, who was to speak at the Century Club on "How to Keep Well," could not appear because of illness.

THE CALIFORNIA (PA.) SENTINEL

●

A patient was convalescing from an appendectomy. A friend came to see him. "How you doing?"

"I'm doing all right, but the day after the operation they opened me up again to take a sponge out of me they left in there. Yesterday they opened me up again and took out a scalpel that they forgot."

Just then the doctor walked in. "Has anyone seen my hat around here?" he asked.

●

Mrs. Millie Mock broke her arm recently. She is recovering nicely under the car of Dr. Leatherman.

THE CALIFORNIA (PA.) SENTINEL

An extremely nervous man carried his twins up to the baptismal font for the christening.

> "What are the names of the little boy and girl?" asked the minister.
>
> "Steak and Kidney," stuttered the embarrassed father.
>
> "What?"
>
> "Their names," corrected the wife icily, "are Kate and Sidney."

●

"Now that you've seen my new son," said the proud new father, "which side of the house do you think he resembles?"

"Well," said his embarrassed bachelor friend, "I came in the front door and really didn't notice either side of the house."

●

HOSTESS (at a dinner party): "What, going already, Professor Bennett? And must you take your dear wife with you?"

PROFESSOR: "Indeed, I'm sorry to say I must!"

●

As a steamer was leaving Athens, a woman went up to the captain and, pointing to the distant hills, inquired:

> "What is that white stuff on those hills?"
>
> "That is snow, madam," replied the captain.
>
> "Well," said the lady, "I thought so myself. But a gentleman just told me it was Greece."

149

At a formal dinner the hostess, who was seated at the far end of the table from a very famous actress, wrote a note to the actress and had the butler deliver it.

The actress couldn't read without her glasses, so she asked the man at her left to read it to her. "It says," he began, 'Dear, do me a favor and please don't neglect the man at your left. I know he's a bore, but talk to him.' "

•

Startling statements found on examination papers:

"Daniel Boone was born in a log cabin he built himself."

"An Indian baby is called a caboose."

"The mother of Abraham Lincoln died in infancy."

They Say It
Happened to —

James Whitcomb Riley and Bill Nye used to go about the country together lecturing. Once when they were traveling by train, Bill Nye, who was very fond of playing jokes on his friend, happened to spy Mr. Riley's ticket protruding from his coat pocket. He reached over and removed it without Riley's knowledge.

When the conductor entered the car for fares, Bill Nye remarked innocently, "Here comes the conductor. Get out your ticket."

Mr. Riley searched first in one pocket and then another, but with no success. At length he turned to his friend and explained that he had lost his ticket, and asked him for a loan since he had spent all his money buying the ticket. But Bill Nye professed to be bankrupt also.

The conductor was fast nearing their seat and the situation was becoming acute, when Bill Nye innocently suggested a way out. "I tell you what, Riley," he said, "just crawl down under the seat and I'll put my coat over you and he'll never know you're there."

Riley was a small man and the situation was desperate: the conductor was almost upon them. Hurriedly he followed Nye's suggestion. When the conductor reached their seat Bill Nye held out both their tickets.

"*Two* fares?" asked the conductor in doubt.

"Yes," solemnly answered the wicked Bill Nye.

"Two?" repeated the train official. "Who's the other one for?"

With a mischievous twinkle in his eye, Bill Nye bent over, lifted the coat from his friend and said,

"It's for my friend here, but he's a little queer. He prefers to ride under the seat."

152

Daniel Webster, the great American statesman, was once sued by his butcher for a very much overdue bill. Before the suit was settled he met the butcher on the street, and to the butcher's embarrassment said, "Why have you not sent around for my order?"

"Why, Mr. Webster," said the man. "I did not think you wanted to deal with me when I brought this suit."

"Tut, tut," said Webster, "sue all you wish, but for heaven's sake don't try to starve me to death!"

●

Gutzon Borglum, the sculptor who created the tremendous Mount Rushmore Memorial in South Dakota, was once asked if he considered his work perfect in every detail.

"Not today," he replied. "The nose of Washington is an inch too long. It's better that way, though. It will erode to be exactly right in ten thousand years."

●

When Calvin Coolidge was a boy, an acquaintance tried to borrow a couple of dollars from him—and was turned down. When Coolidge was President the same person visited the White House and renewed his request for a couple of dollars. Again Coolidge refused. The chum drawled, in reluctant admiration,

"I got to hand it to you, Cal; success ain't changed you a bit!"

153

Gary Cooper was asked during an interview if he uses any word other than his famous "Yup."

"Yup," replied Gary.

"What is it?" asked the newsman.

"Giddy-up!" said Cooper.

•

Walking with a friend one day, Fritz Kreisler passed a large fish shop where a fine catch of codfish, with mouths open and eyes staring, were arranged in a row. Kreisler suddenly stopped, looked at them, and clutching his friend by the arm, exclaimed:

"Heavens! That reminds me—I should be playing at a concert!"

RED GRANGE: "I once carried a hundred-pound load on my back for a mile."

FAN: "It got heavier with every step, I bet."

RED GRANGE: "No—it was ice."

A very amusing story, still going the rounds, is told about Calvin Coolidge when he was Vice-President. The Coolidges lived in the Willard Hotel in Washington. A fire alarm in the middle of the night brought every guest into the lobby, in a variety of negligees and fancy pajamas. Mr. Coolidge speedily surmised that there was no danger and started to trudge back to his room. "Nothing doing!" said the fire marshal, "get back in that lobby!"

"You are speaking to the Vice-President," said Coolidge with some dignity.

"Okay, then," said the marshal. "Go ahead." A moment later he called suspiciously, "What are you Vice-President of?"

"The United States," said Coolidge.

"Come right back here!" ordered the marshal. "I thought you were Vice-President of the hotel."

●

THOMAS JEFFERSON: "What did Franklin say when he discovered electricity in lightning?"

GEORGE WASHINGTON: "Nothing, he was too shocked."

155

In the course of one of his lecture trips Mark Twain arrived at a small town. Before dinner, he went to a barber shop to be shaved.

"You're a stranger?" asked the barber.

"Yes," Mark Twain replied, "this is the first time I've been here."

"You chose a good time to come," the barber continued. "Mark Twain is going to lecture tonight. You'll go, I suppose?"

"Oh, I guess so."

"Have you bought your ticket?"

"Not yet."

"But everything is sold out. You'll have to stand."

"How very annoying!" Mark Twain said, with a sigh. "I never heard of such luck! I *always* have to stand when that fellow lectures."

Gobs of Humor

A pink-cheeked young Ensign reported for duty on a battleship. The gruff old Captain stared at him in disapproval.

"Well!" he said at last. "I guess they decided to send the fool of the family to sea."

"No, sir, not at all," said the Ensign. "That custom has been stopped since your time, sir."

FIRST MATE: "Have you cleaned the deck and polished the brasses?"

GOB: "Yes, sir, and I've swept the horizon with my telescope."

●

The proprietor of a restaurant was reprimanding a careless waiter. "During dinner," he said, "you spilled soup on the Admiral's coat."

"But the Admiral didn't mind, sir, it was Navy Bean soup," answered the waiter.

●

SAILOR: "This coffee tastes like mud."

COOK: "It should. It was ground this morning."

●

A sailor went wearily into the barber shop early one morning and slumped down in a chair. "Give me a shave," he said.

The barber told him that he was too far down in the chair for a shave.

"All right," said the sailor with a sigh, "give me a haircut."

●

The captain of H.M.S. DIAMOND by some navigation error hit the cruiser SWIFTSURE bows on. As the SWIFTSURE went astern, the admiral signaled:

"What do you intend to do now?"

"Buy a farm!" was the reply from the DIAMOND's captain.

A dim-witted girl was visiting a sailor in the hospital.

"Where were you wounded?" she asked.

"In the Solomons, miss," he answered.

"How terrible!" she exclaimed. "Are they any better?"

The sailor came on board carrying a cardboard box punched full of holes.

"What's in the box?" asked his shipmate.

"A cat," said the sailor.

"What do you want of a cat aboard ship?"

"I dream of mice every night, and I'm scared of mice. I've brought along a cat to catch them."

"But you only imagine the mice!"

"Ah, yes," said the sailor. "But the cat in this box is imaginary, too!"

FIRST GOB (in his first battle at sea): "The enemy ships are thick as peas. What shall we do?"

SECOND GOB: "Shell them, of course."

•

MESS COOK: "Did you say you wanted these eggs turned over?"

DISGUSTED GOB: "Yes! Turn them over to a museum!"

•

A sailor was bragging to his girl. "A shell fragment went right through my chest," he boasted.

"Goodness!" she said. "How did it miss your heart?"

"My heart was in my throat at the time," said the sailor modestly.

OLD LADY (stopping a wounded sailor on the street):
"How were you wounded, poor man?"
SAILOR: "By an enemy shell, madam."
OLD LADY: "Did it explode?"
SAILOR: "No. It followed me up the gangplank and
bit me."

●

A naval officer, who had been very strict with his
men, fell overboard. He was rescued by a deck hand.

"What can I do to reward you, my good
fellow?" asked the officer.

"The best way, sir," said the deck hand, "is to
say nothing about it. If the other fellows knew I'd
pulled you out, they'd chuck me in."

161

BRIEFING OFFICER: "Why is it important not to lose your head in an attack?"
GREEN GOB: "Because then I wouldn't have any place to put my cap."

●

The teacher called on little Charlie. "Tell me what you know about George Washington. Was he a soldier or sailor?"

"I think he was a soldier," replied Charlie.

"Why do you think he was a soldier?"

"I seen a picture of him when he crossed the Delaware and any sailor knows enough not to stand up in a rowboat."

●

The chaplain aboard a troop ship said that on the next Sunday he would preach a special sermon. Before then he wanted all the sailors to read the seventeenth chapter of St. Mark. The next Sunday he asked how many sailors had done as he asked. Nearly all of them raised their hands.

"Splendid!" said the chaplain. "My sermon will be on honesty. There are only sixteen chapters in the book of St. Mark."

●

FIRST SAILOR (at mess): "I'm hungry enough to eat a horse."
SECOND SAILOR: "That's what we're getting in a few minutes."

An officer on board a battleship was drilling his men.

"I want every man to lie on his back, put his legs in the air and move them as though he were riding a bicycle," he explained. "Now begin!" After a few minutes one of the men stopped.

"Why did you stop, Smith?" demanded the officer.

"If you please," said Smith, "I'm freewheeling for a while."

"We're a tough outfit," boasted the Marine. "We eat our steak raw and our beans with the shells on. We boil our coffee until it's so thick you can't stir it with a spoon."

"That so?" drawled the Gob. "Well, in the Navy, when we make coffee, we drop the anchor in, and if it sinks, we put in more coffee."

163

Once upon a time there were two naval recruits. Now there are gobs of them.

•

CAPTAIN: "If the boat foundered, whom would you save first, the children or me?"
READY-WITTED GOB: "Me."

•

BARBER: "Haven't I shaved you before, sir?"
SAILOR: "No, I got that scar at Guadalcanal."

Musical Monkeyshines

An old man at a party bowed his head and wept quietly but profusely while a young lady sang the plaintive ballad, "My Old Kentucky Home," in a high soprano voice.

The hostess tiptoed up to him and inquired sympathetically, "Pardon me, are you a Kentuckian?"

"No, madam," the tearful one replied, "I'm a musician."

PAUL: "My brother can play the piano by ear."
SAUL: "That's nothing. My grampaw fiddles with his whiskers."

●

Moisha Rabinovoff began his musical education almost before he could talk. For over twenty years he studied in practically every conservatory in the world. After that he played in concerts in every big European capital—London, Vienna, Rome, Paris. Finally he came to New York to play under Leopold Stokowski. On the first day when he was playing with Stokowski, the great conductor noticed he had a grouchy look on his face.

"Hah!" he thought. "This guy is a sourpuss."

"Why have you got that sour look on your face?" Stokowski demanded. "Don't you like me?" he continued.

"It's not that," answered Rabinovoff.

"Maybe you don't like the other musicians?"

"No, it isn't that."

"Well, maybe you don't like the piece we're playing?"

"No, it's not that."

"Maybe you don't like Carnegie Hall?"

"That isn't it."

"Well, there must be *something* wrong. What is it?"

"*I just don't like music!*" exploded Rabinovoff.

166

DAN: "Did you hear that Jones is making a hundred dollars a night playing the violin?"

NAN: "Imagine! Twenty-five dollars a string!"

DAN: "Yeah, if I were him I'd get a harp."

•

FRED: "You say your son plays the piano like Paderewski?"

TED: "Yes. He uses both hands."

•

DOPEY: "What is your occupation?"

DOPIER: "I used to be an organist."

DOPEY: "And why did you give it up?"

DOPIER: "The monkey died."

•

Walter Damrosch, composer of the opera CYRANO DE BERGERAC, arrived one day at the Met to see his opera. Due to the sudden illness of the tenor, LA BOHÈME was substituted for CYRANO without notifying Damrosch. The latter sat quietly through the first act, then turned to the manager and asked, "Who changed the scenery?"

•

HOSTESS: "They tell me you love music."

GUEST: "Yes, I do. But never mind—keep right on playing."

•

VISITOR: "Does your son play on the piano?"

MOTHER: "No. Not yet. He can't climb that high."

167

GUEST at a musicale: "That's a very, very difficult number that contralto is struggling with!"
OTHER GUEST: "*Difficult?* I wish it were downright *impossible!*"

●

PRETTY YOUNG STUDENT: "Professor Boschovich, do you think I will ever be able to do anything with my voice?"
WEARY TEACHER: "Well it might come in handy in case of fire or shipwreck."

●

POLITE VISITOR: "Your Georgie is making really good progress with his violin since I heard him last. He is beginning to play quite nice tunes."
GEORGIE'S MOTHER: "Oh, do you really think so? His father and I were afraid that we'd merely got used to it."

 168

Legal Giggles

LAWYER: "Among other things, your uncle left you over five hundred clocks."
HEIR: "Oh, dear! It will take a long time to wind up his estate, won't it?"

169

The lawyer came over to the railroad station when his client sent a messenger, and found a doctor setting the client's leg in splints.

"How did you break your leg, Tom?" asked the lawyer.

"Do you see those six steps over there?" asked Tom.

"Yes," said the lawyer.

"Well, I didn't!" said Tom.

A man was suing his wife for assault.

"She hit me with an oak leaf," he said.

"Surely *that* wouldn't have hurt you!" said the Judge.

"It sure did!" said the man. "It was an oak leaf from the dining-room table!"

170

BURGLAR (just released from jail): "Thanks, Judge. I'll drop in on you some time."

JUDGE: "All right, but make it in the daytime, please."

•

MIKE: "Why does a judge have so little time left for himself?"

IKE: "Because he's so busy, I guess."

MIKE: "Wrong! It's because he hands out so much time to other people."

•

JUDGE: "You say you robbed the delicatessen because you were hungry. With all that food around, why didn't you make yourself a sandwich instead of robbing the cash register?"

PRISONER: "I'm a proud man, Judge. I like to pay for what I eat."

171

In a back-woods domestic-relations court the judge listened carefully to both sides in a case against an elderly man who was charged by his wife with non-support.

After all the evidence was in, the judge told the defendant:

"You haven't taken proper care of this good woman, and I'm going to grant her forty dollars a month."

The defendant beamed with pleasure. "That's mighty nice of Your Honor," he said, "and I'll give her a dollar or two from time to time myself."

●

Have you heard the story of the rancher who had occasion to telephone the legal firm of Rasmussen, Rasmussen, Rasmussen and Rasmussen? The conversation went as follows:

"Hello. I'd like to talk to Mr. Rasmussen."

"Mr. Rasmussen is in court arguing a case."

"Oh. Then I'll talk to Mr. Rasmussen."

"Mr. Rasmussen can't come to the phone. He's in conference with an important client."

"Oh. Then I'll talk to Mr. Rasmussen."

"Mr. Rasmussen isn't in today. He's playing golf at South Hills."

"Oh. In that case, can I talk to Mr. Rasmussen?"

"Speaking."

"I'll have to give you ten days in jail or twenty dollars," said the judge.

"I'll take the twenty dollars, Judge," said the prisoner.

●

JUDGE: "How could you swindle people who trusted you?"

PRISONER: "But Judge, people who don't trust you can't be swindled!"

●

LAWYER: "Why did you run away from the scene of the accident?"

CLIENT: "I was running to stop a fight."

LAWYER: "But nobody was fighting!"

CLIENT: "Me and the other driver were!"

●

CLIENT: "My wife's been throwing things at me ever since we were married."

LAWYER: "But why didn't you complain before?"

CLIENT: "This is the first time she's ever hit me."

JUDGE: "Have you ever appeared as a witness before?"

JOE: "Yes, your honor."

JUDGE: "In what suit?"

JOE: "My tan gabardine."

●

Sammy Topper was a bit of a smart-aleck and practical joker, and frequently found himself before the local judge in his small town.

This time the judge told him indignantly, "Look now! You've been warned lots of times. But I'm sorry for your poor long-suffering family, so I'll just fine you now . . . but if this happens again tomorrow, I'll toss you in jail."

"I get it," said Sam. "Fine today . . . cooler tomorrow."

Hillbilly Hoaxes

HILLBILLY (to four-year-old son): "Ira, quit pointin' that thar gun at yore little brother. Hit might go off and kill one of them hawgs he's playin' with."

•

SOCIAL WORKER: "Goodness! doesn't your little boy swear terribly?"

HILLBILLY MAMA: "Yes'm, he sure does. He don't put no expression in it at all."

UNCLE BOSKIE: "I've got a cow I want to sell you, Oscar."

UNCLE OSCAR: "Yeah? Would she fit into my herd?"

UNCLE BOSKIE: "No; I dunno as she would."

UNCLE OSCAR: "Does she give lots of milk?"

UNCLE BOSKIE: "No; I can't say as she gives lots of milk, but I can tell you this: she's a kind, gentle, good-natured old cow, and if she's *got* any milk she'll *give* it to you."

•

MA SNOOKER, a backwoods woman, the soles of whose feet had been toughened by a lifetime of shoe-lessness, was standing in front of her cabin fireplace one day when her husband addressed her.

PA SNOOKER: "You'd better move your foot a mite, Maw; you're standing on a live coal."

MA SNOOKER: "Which foot, Paw?"

•

A hillbilly on a construction job stood reading a letter to another hillbilly. His ears were stopped up with cotton, stuck on with adhesive tape.

The boss came over and said, "What kind of horse-play are *you* two fellows up to?"

"My buddy here," said the hillbilly, "got this here letter his gal writ him, boss, but he kain't read, so he gets me to read it for him, but he stops up my ears so's I kain't hear what his girl writ him."

176

A hillbilly walked into a hotel and registered for a room. The bellhop took his bags and led him across the lobby to the elevator. As they were going up, the new guest took a quick look around and complained, "It sure is an awful small room for five dollars!"

•

Hotel clerk in big city: "Why don't you wipe the mud off your shoes when you come in here?"
Hillbilly: "*What* shoes?"

•

Tourist: "I see you raise hogs almost exclusively about here. Do you find that they pay better than corn and potatoes?"
Hillbilly (slowly): "Wal, no, ma'am; but yer see, ma'am, hawgs don't need no hoeing."

•

First hillbilly: "My Uncle Boskie wants me to he'p him with his income tax."
Second hillbilly: "*You* help him? Why, how can *you* help him—you can't even read or write."
First hillbilly: "Oh, he don't want me to read ner write. He wants me to pay it fer him."

•

Uncle Oscar: "What became of the hired man you got from the city?"
Uncle Boskie: "He crawled under a mule to see why it didn't go."

A hillbilly was complaining about the housing shortage. "I wouldn't mind having all my kinfolk living with me," he moaned. "If it wasn't for their doggone *pets*! Cousin Boskie has six dogs, Aunt Omalia has nine cats. And when they all get to fightin', it disturbs Uncle Jasper's eight hogs so bad, they wake up cousin Chick's dozen goats. It's terrible, especially since the windows are always down."

"Why don't you raise your windows?" asked a friend.

"*What!*" objected the hillbilly, "and let my thirteen buzzards escape!"

POLICEMAN (to hillbilly who has been whipping his horse): "Don't whip him, man—*talk* to him!"
HILLBILLY (to horse, by way of opening the conversation): "*I* come from up in the Cumberland mountains. Where *you* from?"

Egging on
the Elders

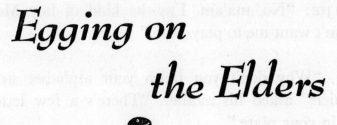

FOND GRANDMA: "Dear, I have a real treat for you. I'm going to take you to the fair and let you ride on the merry-go-round!"
MODERN CHILD: "All right, Grandma, I don't mind, if it will amuse you."

179

VISITOR: "Are you a good boy, Benjie?"
BENJIE: "No, ma'am. I'm the kind of boy Mom doesn't want me to play with."

•

"Why don't you finish your alphabet soup, Daniel?" asked his mother. "There's a few letters left in your plate."

"I know, but they spell spinach," answered Danny firmly.

•

TOMMY: "Pop, can you help me with this arithmetic?"
POP: "I could, but it wouldn't be right, would it?"
TOMMY: "No, I don't suppose so—but you could try, anyhow!"

•

The scoutmaster was very bossy, but he did insist that the boys should have good food at camp. One day he saw two Scouts carrying a large soup kettle.

"Get me a spoon. I want to taste that," he ordered. The boys started to object, but the scoutmaster broke in, "Now, don't give me any arguments. Do as I say!"

They brought a spoon, and he took a large mouthful. Sputtering angrily, he yelled, "You don't call this *soup*, do you!"

"No, sir," one of the Scouts answered. "We *tried* to explain. It's dishwater."

"I'll be good for a nickel, Mother," coaxed little George hopefully.

"Oh, Georgie," replied his mother, "why can't you be like your big brother? He isn't good for a penny. He's good for nothing."

•

A very prim old lady had a few words of advice for her granddaughter. "My dear," she said, "I wish you would do something for me. There are two words I wish you would promise me never to use. One is 'swell' and the other is 'lousy.' Would you promise me that?"

"Why sure, Granny," said her granddaughter. "What are the words?"

•

JOHNNY: "Mom, what was the name of the last station our train stopped at?"

MOTHER: "Don't bother me, I don't know. Don't you see I'm reading?"

JOHNNY: "Well, it's too bad you don't know, because Little Brother got off there."

•

"Didn't you promise me to be a good boy?"

"Yes, Father."

"And didn't I promise you no spending money if you weren't?"

"Yes, Father. But since I've broken my promise, you sure don't have to keep yours."

181

MOTHER: "What do you want to take your cod-liver oil with this morning, Elmer?"
ELMER: "A fork."

●

Young Billy had been to a birthday party, and, knowing his weakness, his mother looked him straight in the eye and said, "I hope you didn't ask Mrs. Parker for a second piece of cake?"

"No," replied Billy. "I told Mrs. Parker I wanted the recipe so you could make some like it, and she gave me two more pieces without my asking at all!"

Boy meets Girl

MOLL: "I dreamed about the funniest thing last night. Wasn't it a funny dream?"

PAUL: "How do *I* know what your dream was about?"

MOLL: "You *ought* to know. You were in it!"

CLEO: "What makes you like Pauline so much?"
LEO: "Nutty haircut, goofy manners, no brains, and too much make-up."
CLEO: "Why, I'm astonished! That certainly describes most of the girls, but surely not *Pauline*!"
LEO: "I know it—that's why I like her so much."

•

DAN: "Do you know the difference between taxis and a bus?"
NAN: "No."
DAN: "Good—then we'll take a trolley."

•

SAUL: "Say, I hear that Jack kissed you last night!"
MOLL: "He did not! And besides, he promised not to tell."

•

"I'd like a box of pencils," said the high-school boy to the clerk in the stationery shop.
"Hard or soft?"
"Soft. They're for writing love letters."

•

Willis called on Phyllis on date night, carrying a package under his arm.
"What have you got there?" said Phyllis.
"Do you like candy?" said Willis.
"I love it," said Phyllis.
"Well, I brought a pan," said Willis, "let's make fudge."

😃 184

They were strolling through a country lane when Claude got romantic. "Ah Maude, look at the cow and the calf rubbing noses in the pasture. That sight makes me want to do the same," he said softly.

"Well, go ahead," his girl answered, "it's *your* cow."

•

ESKIMO: "What would you say, darling, if I told you I pushed my dog team for a thousand miles through ice and snow just to tell you that I love you?"

ESKIMOETTE: "I'd say that was a lot of mush."

•

A fellow was having his first date with a new girl. Things were going along pretty well, as they rode along in his car, when she turned to him and coyly asked: "Do you want to see where I was operated on?"

"Why—uh—yeah. Sure!" he gulped.

"Well, all right," said the girl. "We're just two blocks from the hospital now."

•

FRESH YOUNG MAN in an elegant roadster: "How about a little ride, cutie?"

BRIGHT YOUNG THING: "Are you going north?"

FRESH YOUNG MAN: "Yes, I am."

BRIGHT YOUNG THING: "Good! Give my regards to the Eskimos."

185

DORA: "My sweetie took me down to the picture show last night and we had to ride on a crowded streetcar. Gee! Was he mad!"

NORA: "Because you had to ride on the crowded streetcar?"

DORA: "Well, that's part of the reason, but the thing that made him the sorest was that there was only one seat when we got on, so I had to stand up all the way downtown."

●

There was a young man so benighted,
He never knew when he was slighted;
    He would go to a party,
    And eat just as hearty,
As if he'd been really invited!

●

Why should pretty girls set a good example?
    Because boys are so apt to follow them.

●

GIRL, on the phone: "Is Hugh there?"

KID SISTER, answering: "Hugh *who*?"

GIRL: "Yoo-hoo yourself!"

●

BOB came to class with a black eye.

JIM: "Who gave you that shiner?"

BOB: "My girl friend."

JIM: "I thought she was out of town."

BOB: "I thought that too."

CLAUDE: "Going to have dinner anywhere tonight?"

MAUDE, eagerly: "Why, no, not that I know of."

CLAUDE: "Gee, you'll be awfully hungry by morning!"

•

NEW DATE: "I said, you *have* been out with worse-looking fellows than I am, haven't you?"

POPULAR GIRL: "I heard you the first time. I was trying to think."

•

SWEET YOUNG THING to suitor: "If people ask what I see in you, Herbert, what shall I tell them?"

•

JOHNNY: "Lawrence is just bashful. Why don't you give him a little encouragement."

BONNIE: "Encouragement? *He* needs a cheering section!"

•

PRETTY GIRL at concert: "What's that book the conductor keeps looking at?"

INTELLECTUAL DATE: "That's the score of the overture, of course!"

PRETTY GIRL, excitedly: "Oh, really? Who's winning?"

•

JACK: "Betty doesn't seem to be very intelligent."

JOHN: "No, she didn't pay any attention to me, either."

187

NEW BOYFRIEND: "I'll only marry a girl that can cook well, keep our home attractive, and help me save my money."

ANNOYED GIRLFRIEND: "Fine. You must meet our maid—she's got all those requirements."

●

YOUNG MAN: "Mr. Jones, your daughter has promised to be my wife."

MR. JONES: "That's your own fault—what else did you expect if you kept hanging round here every night?"

Regional Roundup

TOURIST (to Indian in heart of reservation): "White man glad to see red man. White man hope big chief feel tip-top this morning."
INDIAN (calling to a friend): "Hey, Joe, come here and listen to this square. He's really hep!"

189

Uncle Ike Hubbard was once eating supper at the roundup wagon and at the same time complaining about the grub. Finally the cook got so sore that he became quite sarcastic.

"Do you think you kin manage to eat the biscuits, Uncle Ike?" he said with strained sweetness.

"They ain't so bad," answered Uncle Ike. "If you put a lot o' this butter on 'em you can't taste 'em quite so much. 'Course, you can taste the butter, but I'm purty strong myself, as the feller says, and anyhow, your coffee's weak enough to bring up the general average."

●

A tourist traveling through western Kansas saw a man sitting by the ruins of a house that had been blown away.

"Was this your house, my friend?" he asked sympathetically.

"Yep."

"Any of your family blown away with the house?"

"Yep, wife and four kids."

"Great Scott, man, why aren't you hunting for them?"

"Well, stranger, I've been in this country quite a spell. The wind's due to change this afternoon. So I figure I might as well wait here till it brings 'em back."

A tourist driving through Maine wasn't sure he was on the right road. He stopped his car and asked a farmer plowing a field, "Which way is it to Bar Harbor, please?"

"Don't know," the farmer answered.

"Well, then, which way is it to Boothbay Harbor?" the tourist asked.

"Don't know."

In irritation the tourist snapped, "Don't you know *anything*?"

"Well," said the farmer, "*I* ain't lost."

●

"Is this a healthy town?" asked a tourist from New York of a native of Enterprise, Oregon.

"It sure is," replied the native. "When I came here, I hadn't the strength to say a word; I had hardly a hair on my head; I couldn't walk across the room, even with help; I even had to be lifted in and out of bed."

"That's wonderful!" exclaimed the tourist. "How long have you been here?"

"I was born here."

●

Talkative lady tourist: "Shame on you! A big man like you catching poor little helpless fish!"

Vermont fisherman: "Well, if this fish had kept his mouth shut, he wouldn't be on the end of this hook."

A group of tourists in New Mexico came upon an Indian brave riding a pony. A heavily burdened squaw walked beside him.

"Why doesn't the squaw ride?" asked a tourist of the brave.

"She got no pony."

•

An old Vermont storekeeper was dying, and his sorrowful family was assembled at his bedside.

"Is Ma here?" he asked wearily.

"Yes, Zeke," she replied.

"And my oldest son, Aaron?"

"Yes."

"And the other four boys?"

"Yes."

"And all the girls?"

"Yes, Zeke."

The dying man shot up to a sitting position. "What's the big idea?" he shouted. "Who's tending the store?"

•

Some friends were trying to cheer an old Oklahoma cowman who had lost everything he had, including his home.

"You don't need to sympathize with me," he said. "*I'm* all right. I'll come back. I came here fifty years ago with only sixty-five cents and asthma, and I still got the asthma."

A tourist stopped at a combination service station and general store in the back country. While his car was being serviced, he noticed an oldtimer basking in the sun holding a short piece of rope in his hand.

The tourist walked over to him and asked, "What have you there?"

"This is a weather gauge, sonny."

"How can you possibly tell the weather with a piece of rope?" the tourist wanted to know.

"It's simple, sonny. When it swings back and forth it's windy. When it gets wet, it's raining."

●

A mob in Montana once hanged a man because he was supposed to have stolen a horse. After quite a few hours, one of the men broke the news to the dead man's widow in this manner:

"We hanged Sam for stealing a horse, but it turns out he didn't do it after all, so I guess the joke's on us."

●

Two Indians were riding at eighty miles an hour.
FIRST INDIAN: "I think we should slow down."
SECOND INDIAN: "Why?"
FIRST INDIAN: "Because I think we must be getting near the reservation."
SECOND INDIAN: "Why?"
FIRST INDIAN: "Because we're hitting too many Indians."

193

A visitor from New York was visiting a Californian. They were standing out in the open.

"Looks like rain," said the New Yorker.

"Won't rain here," replied the Californian.

"Well, look at those clouds up there."

"Those clouds don't mean anything. They're empty. They're coming back from Florida."

What was the greatest feat of strength ever performed in the United States?

Wheeling West Virginia.

Two close-mouthed Vermont farmers met each other every morning for twenty years in the village store without ever speaking to each other.

One day, Farmer Perkins turned down the street when he went out, instead of up the street as usual.

"Where ya goin'?" asked his startled neighbor.

"None o' yer durn business," snapped Perkins. "And I wouldn't tell yer *that* much if yer warn't an old friend."

Quick Quips

"What do you believe is the reason for your long life, Uncle Ebenezer?" asked the reporter on Uncle Ebenezer's 102nd birthday.

Uncle Ebenezer thought for a moment or two, then, "Well, I guess it's because I was born a long time back, I guess," he said reflectively.

A woman came up to a policeman and said:

"Oh, officer! There's a man following me and I think he must be crazy."

The officer took a good look at her. "Yes," he answered, "he must be!"

•

What always has an eye open but can't see anything?

A needle.

•

A night watchman heard noises in the dark warehouse. Drawing his revolver, he went to the door and called,

"Come out with your hands up, so I can see who you *are*. If you don't, I'll come in and see who you *were*."

•

What word is always pronounced wrong?

Wrong.

•

Why does a chicken cross the road?

For fowl purposes.

•

What is the best material for kites?

Flypaper.

•

"I wish *I* had a pretty, intelligent and helpful wife," said the bachelor.

"So do I," said the husband.

196

ELEVATOR BOY: "Here's your floor, son."
INDIGNANT PASSENGER: "*Son!* How dare you call me that!"
ELEVATOR BOY: "Well, I brought you up, didn't I?"

●

"This tonic will grow hair on a billiard ball."
"Who *wants* hair on a billiard ball?"

●

DOPEY: "Why did the cow get a divorce?"
DOPIER: "She got a bum steer."

●

What is worse than finding a worm in an apple?
Finding only half a worm.

●

The bald-headed man would like very much to part with his comb and brush.

●

Didja hear about the comic who told the same jokes three nights running—he wouldn't dare tell them standing still.

●

Two boll weevils came from the country to the city. One became rich and famous. The other remained the lesser of the two weevils.

●

Have you heard of the woman who was such a good cook she graduated from cooking school with flying crullers?

A visitor at a state prison asked one of the prisoners, "What's your name?"

"9742," the prisoner sneered.

"Is that your *real* name?"

"Naw," he said, "just me pen name."

●

How many peas in a pint?

One.

●

Why would a barber rather shave ten men from New York than one from San Francisco?

Because he would get ten times as much money.

Dizzy-
Daffy-
Nitions

TEACHER: "Frankie, can you define nonsense?"
FRANKIE: "Yes, teacher—an elephant hanging over a cliff with his tail tied to a buttercup."

●

What is a professor?

A textbook wired for sound.

199

What's the difference between a mother and a barber?

> *The barber has razors to shave. The mother has shavers to raise.*

•

What is the difference between a beached ship and an airplane?

> *One grounds on the land, and the other lands on the ground.*

•

BENNY: "What part of an automobile kills the most people?"
KENNY: "The nut behind the wheel!"

•

What makes more noise than a pig caught under a fence?

> *Two pigs.*

•

What is the difference between fog and a falling star?

> *One is mist on earth, the other is missed in heaven.*

•

An egoist is someone always me-deep in conversation.

•

TEACHER: "George, what is a synonym?"
GEORGIE: "A synonym is a word you use when you can't spell the other one."

TEACHER (to bring out the idea of size): "Mention a difference between an elephant and a flea."
TOMMY: "Well, an elephant can have fleas, but a flea can't have elephants."

●

What is the difference between the earth and the sea?

One is dirt-y, the other is tide-y.

●

Paul and Saul were trying to define the word "collision."

"Collision," said Paul, "is when two things come together unexpectedly."

"I know," brightly replied Saul. "Twins."

Child's definition: An adult is one who has stopped growing except in the middle.

●

Tomorrow: One of the greatest labor-saving inventions of today.

●

A hard-boiled egg is hard to beat.

●

A dentist is a man with a lot of pull.

 202

Laughs

Across the Oceans

ENGLISHMAN, to visiting AMERICAN: "Odd names your towns have. Such as Hoboken, Skaneateles, Walla Walla, Oshkosh, Albuquerque."

AMERICAN: "I suppose they do sound queer to English ears. Do you live in London all of the time?"

ENGLISHMAN: "No, indeed. I spend part of my time at Chipping Norton, and divide the rest between Bigglewade, Bournemouth, and Leighton Buzzard."

VISITING AMERICAN: "How come you Scotsmen are so thrifty?"
SCOTTISH HOST: "It is a gift."

●

SANDY: "I want a cheap coat hanger."
SALESPERSON: "Here's one for three pence."
SANDY: "Three pence! I want something much cheaper."
SALESPERSON: "The nail department is down two aisles to the left."

●

"Ah, it was different in the old days," whispered the old professor in a café in Warsaw, glancing cautiously around the room. "Then we could lie as we pleased. Now we have to lie as we are told."

●

VISITING AMERICAN TOURIST: "James, I am afraid that, by mistake, I tipped His Lordship instead of you."
ENGLISH BUTLER: "I'll never see the tip now."

●

"Russia," cried the Soviet agriculture expert at a Paris meeting, "is an agricultural paradise, with *four wheat crops* a year."
Incredulous listeners demanded how this could be.

"It's easy," he explained. "We have one from Poland, one from Hungary, one from Czechoslovakia, and one from Russia."

Andrew Carnegie was born in Scotland, and came to America as a boy. When he returned for a visit after he had become one of the richest men in the world, two of his townsmen were discussing the famous visitor.

SANDY: "I hear that Andrew Carnegie is worth $400,000,000!"

MAC: "Weel! He sure must have had a saving woman!"

•

An American in Hong Kong on business, was placed next to a Chinese at a banquet. At the end of the first course, the American turned to his neighbor and said, "Likee soupee?"

The Chinese grunted, "Yes."

At the end of the meat course the American said, "Likee meatee?"

The Chinese again grunted, "Yes."

Then the Chinese man was introduced and spoke eloquently for half an hour in perfect English.

When he sat down he turned to his American neighbor and said, "Likee speechee?"

•

The story is that the Grand Canyon was caused by a Scotsman dropping a dime.

•

MAC: "How much candy can you eat?"

JOCK: "Any given amount."

TIM: "How does your new short-wave radio work?"
CHARLIE: "Perfectly—I got China when I turned it on at three o'clock this morning."
TIM: "China and what else?"
CHARLIE: "Flowerpots, milk bottles, and old shoes."

●

A newspaper correspondent assigned to cover the Paris peace meetings bumped into an old acquaintance whom he knew to be a secret agent.

"Hello," he said. "What are you doing here?"

"Oh, just looking for scraps of information," answered the agent. "And what are you doing here?"

"Oh, I'm just looking for information of scraps," replied the correspondent.

●

GUIDE, on a safari in Africa: "Quick, m'lord! Shoot that leopard on the spot!"
LORD KILBRACKEN: "Be specific, my man: *which* spot?"

●

Food is more plentiful in Paris with the summer season, but not so with meat, which accounts for a restaurant patron's complaint to the waiter that his pork chop was too little and too hot.

"Why don't you blow on it?" the waiter none too politely inquired.

"I am afraid to," said the diner. "It might blow away."

😐 206

An immigration officer asked a small Chinese man his name.

"Sneeze," replied the man proudly.

"Is that Chinese?" asked the officer.

"No," said the man, "it's my American name."

"Then," asked the officer, "what is your native name?"

"Ah Choo!" replied the Chinese man.

●

FIRST ACTOR, in a London Club: "I'd rather play to an English audience than an American audience."

SECOND ACTOR: "What's the difference between an Englishman and an American?"

FIRST ACTOR: "Well, an Englishman first laughs out of courtesy; second, when the rest of the audience gets the joke; and third, when he gets it himself."

SECOND ACTOR: "What about an American?"

FIRST ACTOR: "Oh, he never laughs at all—he's heard it before."

207

A fellow, carrying a hundred-pound bomb, got on a London bus and sat down.

"What's that you've got in your lap?" asked the conductor.

"It's a delayed-action bomb I'm taking to the police station," came the answer.

"Coo!" exclaimed the conductor. "You don't want to carry a thing like that on your lap! Put it under the seat!"

●

ENGLISH PROFESSOR, at dinner: "It was Sir Walter Raleigh who first introduced your American turkey into Britain."

AMERICAN GUEST, trying to cut his portion: "And this one must be the very one he introduced."

●

A Frenchman asked a German guest how they told the difference in Germany between an optimist and a pessimist.

"Very simple," the German explained. "The optimist is learning English, the pessimist is learning Russian."

●

A railroad agent in Africa had been bawled out for doing things without orders from headquarters. One day his boss received the following startling telegram: "Tiger on platform eating conductor. Wire instructions."

208

The cockney innkeeper of the HAND AND ᴧOR objected to the way a painter had painted his sign:
    "There ought to be more space between 'and and and and and and 'and and Anchor!"

●

An Arab stood on a weighing machine in the light
    of the lingering day
A counterfeit penny he dropped in the slot and
    silently stole a weigh.

●

AMERICAN TOURIST in France: "Waiter, bring me some of this—see, here on the menu."
WAITER: "Madam, the orchestra is playing it now."

●

FRENCHMAN greeting friend at boat: "Did you have any difficulty with your English in America?"
RETURNING FRIEND: "No—but the Americans did."

●

GUIDE, in England: "This tower goes back to William the Conqueror."
TOURIST: "Why, what's the matter with it? Isn't it satisfactory?"

●

FIRST ENGLISHMAN: "Charley, did you hear that joke about the Egyptian guide who showed some tourists two skulls of Cleopatra—one as a girl and one as a woman?"
SECOND DITTO: "No, let's hear it."

209

George's father was one of those rich self-made men who have no use for learning unless it helps business. But George wanted to go to Paris to learn the language and study art. At last he got permission to leave. Six months later, his father went to Europe on business and visited George in Paris. The boy took him to an expensive restaurant and they had a fine dinner. After coffee he spoke a few words in French to the waiter.

"Is that all the French you've learned?" asked the old man.

"It's enough," George replied. "I told him to give you the check."

•

An Englishman was traveling with an American through the corn belt. "My dear man," he said, "what are you doing with all this corn?"

"Well," said the American, "we eat what we can and what we can't, we can."

The Englishman found this hilarious. As soon as he was back in London he told his friends in the club about the abundance of corn and his question about it. "And you know what the Yankee said?" he asked. " 'We eat as much as we can and what we cannot eat we put into tins.' "

Trip Talk

An excited young man ran madly down the ferry landing, leaped across six feet of water, and landed with a crash on the deck of the ferry.

"Well," he gasped, as he picked himself up, "I made it!"

"What's your hurry?" asked a deck hand. "This boat's comin' *in*."

PASSENGER: "Is this bus on time?"

BUS DRIVER: "No, but we're on the right road."

•

TRAVELER: "How much will you charge to take my baggage to Canal Street?"

TAXI DRIVER: "Half dollar for you, sir. Your luggage goes free."

TRAVELER: "Okay, then. You just take the luggage, and I'll walk."

•

FRANK: "You must have had a terrible accident last night. The front of your car is all smashed in. What did you hit?"

HANK: "Last night I was driving and hit a cow——"

FRANK: "A Jersey cow?"

HANK: "I don't know—I didn't see her license plate."

•

The Browns were just back from a vacation trip to New Jersey.

"How did you find the mosquitoes?" asked a friend.

"I didn't," said Mr. Brown. "*They* found *me*."

•

"Do you have hot and cold water in this hotel?" inquired a visitor.

"Yes, hot in the summer and cold in the winter," the clerk informed her.

212

A city youngster, who was more accustomed to man-made wonders than to the marvels of nature, was taken on a vacation to Niagara Falls. There he saw his first rainbow. As the boy stood and gazed upon the gorgeous sight, he was full of wonder and surprise.

"Mother," he finally exclaimed, "it's certainly beautiful but what does it advertise?"

●

The bore was giving the story of his travels in the Swiss Alps and droned on, and on, and on. At one point he remarked: "There I stood, with the abyss yawning before me."

"Excuse me," interjected a bored listener, "but was that abyss yawning before you got there?"

●

A fat lady with her arms full of bundles wedged herself in the bus and fumbled for her purse in her coat pocket to pay the fare. She struggled and struggled. A man standing next to her suddenly handed her a dime. "Take this, lady," he said unhappily, "and pay your fare. I'm getting tired of you buttoning and unbuttoning my suspender buttons."

●

HOTEL GUEST: "Is there an Encyclopaedia Britannica in the hotel?"

DESK CLERK, politely: "I'm so sorry, sir. We haven't one—but what is it you wish to know?"

213

One night at a party at the Elwells, Mrs. Barker was telling of their novel vacation plan. "You see," said Mrs. Barker, "last year a few of us cooked up such a satisfactory vacation plan that we're going to do it again this year."

"What was it?" asked Mrs. Elwell.

"Well," said Mrs. Barker, "six couples of us pooled our vacation money and rented a big house at the seashore for the season. Each couple spent two weeks there, taking care of the kids. All told, there were seventeen of them."

"Well!" exclaimed Mrs. Elwell. "I wouldn't call taking care of seventeen children a *vacation*— but I suppose the kids loved it."

"Oh," said Mrs. Barker quickly, "those two weeks were a *nightmare*! What *was* a vacation was the ten weeks at home without our kids."

RIDER, on way to station: "Why did they build this station so far out of town?"

DRIVER: "They wanted it to be near the railroad."

HOTEL CLERK (to guest parading through lobby in pajamas): "Here, what are you doing?"

GUEST (awakened): "Oh, I'm *so* sorry! But I'm a somnambulist."

HOTEL CLERK: "Well, you can't walk around here like that, no matter *what* your religion is."

A man rushed off a train and ran up to a little boy standing on the platform.

"We've only got a short stop here," he said. "Here's a quarter. Go in that lunchroom and get me a sandwich, will you? And here's another quarter. Get a sandwich for yourself, too."

The boy was gone so long the man began to get nervous. Just as the conductor hollered "All Aboard!" the kid dashed out of the lunchroom and ran over to the man.

"Here's your quarter," he said. "They only had one sandwich."

●

Have you heard about the man who took a vacation to forget everything? The first night at the hotel he opened his suitcase and discovered he *had* forgotten everything.

●

STUFFY AUNT: "Well, Horace, you haven't honored us with your presence for a long time. Just what brought you to town *this* time?"

HORACE: "Well I just came to see the sights, and thought I'd call on you first."

●

SUMMER BOARDER: "What became of that other windmill that was here last year?"

FARMER: "There was only enough wind for one, so we took it down."

A Spaniard, an American, and a Scotsman were discussing what they would do if they awoke one morning to discover that they were millionaires.

The Spaniard said he would build a bull ring.

The American said he would go to Paris to have a time.

The Scotsman said he would go to sleep again to see if he could make another million.

•

RUSTY: "So you missed your train?"

BUSTER: "Yes!"

RUSTY: "By how much did you miss it?"

BUSTER: "I missed it by just a minute."

RUSTY: "Well, don't get so excited. The way you're carrying on, it's as if you missed it by an hour."

Travel Teasers

Severely jostled in the thundering herd of New York's subway rush hour, a girl was finally crammed among the standees. Her sense of humor was not impaired, however. She poked her face close to the ear of the man standing next to her.

"Look," she demanded tartly, "my rib—is it crushing your elbow?"

217

LADY: "Can you give me a room and bath?"
HOTEL CLERK: "I can give you a room, madam, but you'll have to take your own bath."

●

A train ran off a big bridge recently and no one was killed or injured. How can this be?

> *It ran off the bridge at one end as usual and went on its way along the tracks.*

●

What is it that is found in the very center of America and Australia?

> *The letter* R.

●

Why should a man always wear a watch when he travels in a desert?

> *Every watch has a spring.*

●

Why are weary people like automobile wheels?

> *Because they are tired.*

●

PAUL: "What's your hurry, Saul?"
SAUL: "I'm going to the airport to catch the 5:30 plane."
PAUL: "Well, what's your hurry? It's only 2:30 now."
SAUL: "I *know* that. But I always have to figure on a few dopes stopping me to ask me why I'm hurrying."

😊 218

What is the richest country in the world?

Ireland, because its capital is always Dublin.

●

What is the difference between the North Pole and the South Pole?

All the difference in the world.

●

What state is round at both ends, and high in the middle?

Ohio.

●

When does an automobile go exactly as fast as a train?

When it is on the train.

●

You can always tell the English;
You can always tell the Dutch;
You can always tell the Yankees—
But you cannot tell them much!

●

A midget belonging to a circus got on the sleeper at Chicago to go to New York. He had an upper berth. He went into the diner and drank a large cup of coffee. About two hours later the man in the lower berth rang loudly for the porter.

"Porter!" he shouted. "I can't sleep. Someone is pacing overhead."

A motorist speeding along a highway at eighty miles an hour was stopped by a policeman. "Was I driving too fast?" asked the motorist apologetically.

"Oh no," replied the policeman. "You were flying too low."

"What's the matter with you, are you blind?" said the pedestrian.

"Blind?" snapped the driver. "I *hit* you, didn't I?"

Girls, Girls, Girls

PRETTY YOUNG GIRL, to friend: "Not only has Jack broken my heart and wrecked my whole life, but he has spoiled my entire evening!"

●

A young lady after a broken engagement returned all her friend's letters marked, "Fourth Class Male."

TESS: "I was horseback riding yesterday and from the after-effects I think I'll learn to ride side-saddle."
BESS: "Why do that?"
TESS: "It saves you a little place where you can sit down the next day."

●

ETTA: "Do you believe in free speech?"
GRETTA: "I certainly do."
ETTA: "Then may I make a long distance call on your telephone?"

●

Three girls are under an umbrella, but none of them gets wet. How can this be?

It isn't raining.

●

Ring! Ring!

"Hello, Betty, this is Nettie—are you wearing your pedal pushers tonight?"

"Why, yes, I'm afraid I am."

"Good. Then you won't mind lending me your formal."

●

DORA: "Where is your brother?"
CORA: "He's in the hospital—his girl threw him over."
DORA: "That shouldn't have made him go to a hospital."
CORA: "Yes, but *this* girl threw him over a cliff."

222

BELLA: "Did anyone ever tell you how wonderful you are?"
STELLA: "Don't believe they ever did."
BELLA: "Then where'd you get the idea?"

•

MOLLY, at a picnic: "We've got thousands of things to eat."
POLLY: "Gee—what?"
MOLLY: "Beans."

•

JOAN: "Did Evelyn inherit her beauty?"
JANE: "Yes, her father left her a drug store."

•

TILLY: "He's worth in the neighborhood of Fifty Thousand Dollars, I've heard."
BILLIE: "Good! That's my favorite neighborhood."

•

"Have you seen Sally's new dress?"
"No, what does it look like?"
"Well, in many places it's a lot like Sally."

•

HELEN: "I don't see how football players ever get clean!"
RUTH: "Silly, what do you suppose the scrub teams are for?"

223

MABEL: "How is your new boy friend?"
MARY: "He is very fast with a buck—then he slows down."

•

MARY: "She sure gave you a dirty look."
LOUISE: "Who?"
MARY: "Mother Nature."

•

JOAN: "Hasn't Jack ever married?"
JEAN: "No, I don't think he intends to, because he's studying for a bachelor's degree."

•

BETTY: "Who is that guy with the long hair?"
MARY: "He's the sophomore from Yale."
BETTY: "Oh, I've often heard of those Yale locks."

Goofy Guys

"I went hunting the other day," said Simpson, "and the dogs got in the way of a skunk. Finally they gave up the chase."

"Did they lose the scent?" asked his friend.

"They gave up the skunk, but I don't think they will ever lose the scent," Simpson answered with feeling.

LENNY: "Do you believe it is seven years' bad luck if you break a mirror?"

BENNY: "No, indeed not. My cousin broke one and he didn't have seven years' bad luck."

LENNY: "He didn't?"

BENNY: "No, he was killed in an explosion the same day."

•

"Why is this train late?" an irritated lady asked the conductor.

"Well, lady," explained the conductor, "the trouble is that the train in front is behind and this train was behind before besides."

•

As he paid his hotel bill the departing guest turned and yelled to the bellboy, "Quick, boy, run up to room 999 and see if I left my brief case and overcoat. *Hurry up*, because I've got just six minutes to catch my train."

Four minutes later the bellboy was back, all out of breath. "Yes, sir," he reported, "they're up there."

•

BILLY: "How's your father coming with his new dairy farm?"

SILLY: "Grand. He makes all the cows sleep on their backs."

BILLY: "What's the idea?"

SILLY: "So the cream will be on top in the morning."

Shingles were coming loose on Mr. Lazyman's house, and he complained of the leaks.

"Why don't you mend the roof?" asked the neighbor next door.

"I can't today—it's pouring rain."

"Well, why don't you mend it in dry weather?"

"It don't leak then," said Mr. Lazyman.

●

FARMER: "What are you doing up in that tree, young fellow?"

BOY: "One of your apples fell down, and I'm trying to put it back!"

●

CIRCUS MANAGER: "Well, *now* what's wrong?"

INDIA-RUBBER MAN, pitifully: "Every time the strong man writes a letter he uses me to rub out the mistakes."

●

BELLBOY: "Telegram for Mr. Portocopondolous! Mr. Portocopondolous!"

MR. PORTOCOPONDOLOUS: "Boy! What initial, please?"

●

LOUIE: "How did you like the play last night?"

HUGHIE: "I saw the first act, but not the second."

LOUIE: "Why not?"

HUGHIE: "I couldn't wait that long. It said on the program—second act, two years later."

SCOUTMASTER: "George, are all the rest of the boys out of the woods yet?"

GEORGE: "Yes."

SCOUTMASTER: "All seven of them?"

GEORGE: "Yes, all seven of them."

SCOUTMASTER: "And they're all safe?"

GEORGE: "Yep, they're all safe."

SCOUTMASTER: "Then, by golly, I've shot a deer!"

•

DOPE: "I can climb *anything*."

DUPE (throwing a flashlight beam upward): "Well, then climb that!"

DOPE: "Well—I could. But it would be just like you to turn it off when I was twenty-five feet up. Then where would *I* be!"

•

MAN calling on telephone. "Hello, this is Andy."

DEAF MAN answering: "Eh?"

FIRST MAN: "This is Andy! *A* for Adam, *N* for Ned, *D* for Dan and *Y* for ——"

DEAF MAN, interrupting him: "Yes, yes! I know all you guys, but *which* one is talking *now*?"

•

EDDIE: "My brother stands in front of a mirror with his eyes closed."

TEDDIE: "What for?"

EDDIE: "Oh, he just wants to see what he looks like when he is asleep."

228

A boy was down on his hands and knees looking for something on the sidewalk when a policeman approached.

"What are you doing?" said the cop.

"I lost a silver dollar on Third Avenue," was the answer.

"But this is Fourth Avenue," the cop pointed out. "If you lost the dollar on Third Avenue, why are you looking for it on Fourth?"

"Because there's more light here," said the boy.

●

A hillbilly was taken to the hospital after an accident. He had his temperature taken and was then left alone in the ward until the house doctor made his rounds.

"Well," said the doctor, "how do you feel?"

"Okay, boss."

"Had any nourishment?"

"What did you say?"

"I said, have you taken anything in the way of food?"

"Well, a while ago a lady give me a piece of glass to suck."

●

ACTOR: "Why did you quit the stage?"

COMEDIAN: "Ill health."

ACTOR: "What do you mean, ill health?"

COMEDIAN: "I made people sick."

229

Dope and Dupe stepped out of the plane as it landed in Pittsburgh. Suddenly Dope let out a cry.

"Dupe," he groaned, "I think I've lost my wallet!"

"Did you look in your pockets?" asked Dupe.

"All but one," replied Dope, unhappily.

"Well, for goodness' sake, why don't you look there?"

"Because," Dope moaned, "if it's not there, I'll die!"

●

An applicant for citizenship wasn't too clear about the judge's question, "Do you solemnly swear to support the Constitution?" Finally he answered, "Judge, I'd like to, but I already have a wife and six children in Europe."

Troubles, Troubles, Troubles

A pigeon came home very late for dinner one evening, with his feathers bedraggled, and his eyes bloodshot. "I was out minding my own business," he explained, "when—bingo! I get caught in a badminton game!"

231

A man once decided that he wanted to commit suicide, so he made very elaborate preparations, to be *sure* nothing would defeat his purpose. He went out on a very high bridge, and took along a can of gasoline, a match, a rope, and a revolver.

He tied the rope around his neck, then tied it to the bridge. Next he poured gasoline over his clothes. Then he lit a match to himself. Finally, just as he jumped off the bridge, he shot off his revolver.

The revolver shot cut the rope; his fall into water put out the fire; and if he hadn't known how to swim, he would have drowned!

•

"Oh, did I find a dreamy apartment!" said Mrs. Gush to her friend. "It has a wonderful living room, a wonderful balcony, a wonderful dining room, a wonderful bedroom, and the kitchen—the kitchen is out of this world!"

FRIEND: "Isn't that a little bit inconvenient?"

•

GRACIE ALLEN: "They put my brother in jail for stealing, but it wasn't his fault."

GEORGE BURNS: "Oh, it wasn't his fault?"

GRACIE ALLEN: "No, how did he know the woman didn't mean what she said?"

GEORGE BURNS: "What did the woman say?"

GRACIE ALLEN: "Well, he was helping her house clean and she gave him a rug and told him to beat it."

REPORTER: "What made you risk your life to save your friend?"

BOY HERO: "I *had* to do it. He was wearing my skates."

●

FIRST COMMUNIST: "Nice weather we're having."

SECOND COMMUNIST: "Yeah, but the rich are having it, too!"

A banquet speaker went on and on with his speech. The Mayor nodded, and, after a while, rested his head on the tablecloth. The chairman reached over and bumped him lightly on the head with his gavel.

MAYOR: "Hit me harder—I can still hear him."

Two little boys were playing noisily in a train. The conductor finally told their father that the children must behave or he would make trouble for him. The boy's father said, wearily:

"Trouble—you don't know what trouble *is*! My wife's in the hospital. I have the itch. I am on my way to see my sick mother-in-law; my daughter has just had triplets; one of the boys has just smashed his finger and the other has chewed up our tickets. And that's not all—I just discovered we are on the wrong train."

Whoppers, Whoppers, Whoppers

The New Yorker said, "I once had an old mare that licked the fastest express train on a forty-mile run."

"That's nothing!" said the Texan. "I was out about thirty miles from my house on my farm one day, when a frightful storm came up. I turned the pony's head for home and, do you know, he raced the storm so close for the last ten miles that I didn't feel a drop—while my dog, only ten yards behind, had to swim the whole distance!"

235

A cowboy was raving about his horse. "I got the smartest horse you ever saw!" he declared. "One day while riding I fell off and broke my leg."

"Wait a minute," interrupted another cowboy. "You're not going to tell me he picked you up and put you back in the saddle."

"No, but he dragged me to my bunk, then galloped five miles to get me a doctor. There was only one catch: he came back with a *horse* doctor!"

•

South Dakota is noted for very sudden changes of temperature. One summer day it got so hot that a field of popcorn started popping—it really caused a flurry! The cows in the next field thought it was snowing, and froze to death watching!

•

DOPEY: "My grampa made a scarecrow so terrible that it frightened every single crow off the place."
DOPIER: "You think *that's* something? *I* made one that scared 'em so much they brought back the corn they stole last year!"

•

One year at the Liar's Club meeting where everyone told their biggest whopper the prize was won by a member who merely said: "I never told a lie."

A hunter was out in the forest. It was late in the day and getting colder. A bear appeared. The hunter grabbed his gun—there was no ammunition left! He wiped the sweat off his brow and put it in the gun—it shot out as an icicle and pierced the head of the bear and the bear died of water on the brain!

EXECUTIONER to prisoner: "Have you any last words?"
PRISONER: "Yes! This will be a lesson to me."

•

There once was a lawyer who joined a nudist colony and never had a suit afterwards.

•

POLICEMAN (to boy sitting on top of oak tree): "Hey! What are you doing up there?"
BOY: "I don't know. I must have sat on an acorn."

"It was so cold where we were," boasted the Arctic explorer, "that the candle froze and we couldn't blow it out."

"That's nothing," said his rival. "Where we were the words came out of our mouths in pieces of ice, and we had to fry them to see what we were talking about."

•

An Easterner and a Westerner were walking one day near the foot of one of the Catskill mountains. The Easterner, wishing to impress the visitor, produced a famous echo to be heard in that place. When the echo returned clearly after nearly three minutes, the proud Easterner, turning to the Westerner, exclaimed:

"There, you haven't anything like *that* out your way!"

"Oh, I don't know," said the Westerner, "I guess we can better that. Why, in my camp in the Rockies, when I go to bed I just lean out the window and call out, *'Time to get up; wake up!'* and eight hours afterward the echo comes back and wakes me."

Stretching the Baloney

(We had to fill up these
last few pages *somehow!*)

239

The two tramps were stretched out on the green grass. Above them was the warm sun, beside them was a babbling brook. It was a quiet, restful, peaceful scene.

"Boy," mused the first tramp contentedly, "right now I wouldn't change places with a guy who owns a million bucks!"

"How about five million?" asked his companion.

"Not even for five million," drowsed the first tramp.

"Well," persisted his pal, "how about ten million bucks?"

The first tramp sat up.

"That's different," he admitted. "Now you're talking real dough!"

●

A floorwalker, tired of his job, gave it up and joined the police force. Several months later a friend asked him how he liked his new job. "Well," he replied, "the pay and the hours are good, but what I like best is that the customer is always wrong."

●

"How can I ever show my appreciation?" gushed a woman to a famous lawyer, after he had solved her legal troubles.

"Madam," he replied, "ever since the Phoenicians invented money there's been only one answer to that question."

240

Then there's the story of the angry wife of a movie star who had gone off fishing and left her alone. Asked where her husband might be, she replied, "Just go down to the bridge and look around until you find a pole with a worm on each end!"

•

Hetty, the little daughter of a tire salesman, had seen triplets for the first time in the daily paper.
"Oh, Mummy!" she called out, "What do you think it says here?"
"I can't imagine, dear. What?"
"It tells about a lady that had twins—*and a spare!*"

•

At a dinner for a child star who was a big box-office attraction a movie producer got up, patted the little girl on the head, and said, "We wish to pay homage to our little star." Then, placing his hand on the shoulder of the star's mother, he continued, "But we don't want to forget the goose that laid the golden egg."

•

A little girl at her first church wedding suddenly whispered loudly to her mother: "Mummy, has the lady changed her mind?"
"Why, dear, whatever do you mean?" her mother asked.
"Well, Mummy, she went up the aisle with one man and came back with another!"

"Don't throw banana peels on the edge of the Grand Canyon," cautioned a ranger to a careless tourist. "You don't want somebody to slip and fall three miles, do you?"

•

There was a young lady of Niger
Who smiled as she rode on a tiger.
 They came back from the ride
 With the lady inside
And a smile on the face of the tiger.

•

When the train stopped at the little Southern station, the tourist from the North got out and strolled around a bit. He gazed curiously at a lean animal with scraggy bristles which was rubbing itself against a scrub-oak.

"What do you call *that*?" he asked curiously of a farmer on a hay wagon.

"A razorback hawg, suh," the farmer replied.

"What is he doing, rubbing himself against that tree?"

"He's stropping hisself, suh; jes' stropping hisself."

 242

The book was designed by J. M. KUPFER